Financial Fitness for Life®

Student Workbook

Grades 9-12

Suzanne Gellman
Sharon C. Laux
Authors, Second Edition

John S. Morton
Mark C. Schug
Authors, First Edition

COUNCIL FOR
Economic Education

Teaching Opportunity®

AUTHORS, SECOND EDITION:
Suzanne Gellman
Consumer Economics Specialist
University of Missouri Extension

Sharon C. Laux
Associate Director
University of Missouri-St. Louis Center for Entrepreneurship and Economic Education

AUTHORS, FIRST EDITION:
John S. Morton
Senior Program Officer
Arizona Council on Economic Education

Mark C. Schug
Professor Emeritus
University of Wisconsin, Milwaukee

PROJECT DIRECTOR:
Richard A. MacDonald
Senior Advisor for Program Development
Council for Economic Education
and
Assistant Professor of Economics
St. Cloud State University

PROJECT COORDINATORS:
Christopher Caltabiano
Vice President for Program Administration
Council for Economic Education

Irina Piven
Senior Program Associate
Council for Economic Education

EDITOR:
Richard Western

DESIGN AND LAYOUT:
Jill O'Leske
Impact Design, LLC

Presented by:

Bank of America

This publication was made possible through funding by the Bank of America Charitable Foundation.

ISBN 1-56183-697-0   5 4 3 2 1

Acknowledgments

AUTHOR SUPPORT TEAM:

Janet Bagby
Frederick Douglass High School
Columbia, MO

Lucy Ryder-Duffey
Carnahan High School of the Future
St. Louis, MO

Cindy Evans
Oakville High School
St. Louis, MO

Mindy Nikolaisen
Gateway Institute of Technology High School
St. Louis, MO

Kitty Scott
Our Lady of Fatima School
Benton, AR

CONTENT REVIEWERS:

Kris Bertelsen
St. Charles High School
St. Charles, MN

Nathan Eric Hampton
St. Cloud State University
St. Cloud, MN

Scott Wolla
Federal Reserve Bank of St. Louis
St. Louis, MO

Table of Contents

THEME 4: SPENDING AND CREDIT

THEME 5: SAVING AND INVESTING

Introduction

The Economic Way of Thinking

You may not know much about managing your money. And what you don't know could hurt you. All your life you will be spending, saving, borrowing, and investing. You will make economic decisions as a consumer, a worker, an investor, and a citizen. The choices you make at any point along the way will have major consequences for your future. To mention only a few:

- What occupation should I pursue?
- Should I go to college?
- Should I get a credit card?
- Are all credit cards alike?
- Should I start saving now or wait until I have a better job and a larger income?
- Should I invest in the stock market?
- What stocks or mutual funds should I invest in?

You probably are not ready to make these choices. Many young people are not. The average score earned by high school students on a recent national survey of knowledge about personal finance was 48.3 percent. That's a grade of F in any class, and it is an even lower score than the 51.9 percent earned by high school students 10 years ago. Similarly, high school students also received an "F" on a recent national test about economics. Their average score was only 53 percent (adults scored 70 percent on the same test).

One of the most important lessons you will learn in studying economics and personal finance is that incentives matter. So, what's the incentive for studying personal finance? For openers, what you learn might make you rich. Achieving personal wealth involves planning and making sound financial choices–about getting an education,

 1

saving early and often, comparison shopping, developing a money-management plan, and shopping for the best loan. You might be surprised to know that most millionaires in this country did not get rich quick by winning the lottery or inheriting money from a relative. The became rich by making sound choices, including these:

- Getting a good education.
- Working long, hard, and smart.
- Learning money-management skills.
- Living below their means.
- Investing in the stock market for the long term.
- Gathering information, developing criteria, and considering the alternatives before making decisions.

Learning to make smart choices is not rocket science. It might take some work, but you can learn to do it. Your efforts now can have a big payoff later. How about starting on your first million bucks right now?

NAME: _____ CLASS PERIOD: _____

The Millionaire Game Score Sheet

1. **True or False Score   (-5 or +5)**
    (circle one)   (Millionaire card -10 or +10)   _____

2. **True or False Score   (-5 or +5)**
    (circle one)   (Millionaire card -10 or +10)   _____

3. **True or False Score   (-5 or +5)**
    (circle one)   (Millionaire card -10 or +10)   _____

4. **True or False Score   (-5 or +5)**
    (circle one)   (Millionaire card -10 or +10)   _____

5. **True or False Score   (-5 or +5)**
    (circle one)   (Millionaire card -10 or +10)   _____

6. **True or False Score   (-5 or +5)**
    (circle one)   (Millionaire card -10 or +10)   _____

7. **True or False Score   (-5 or +5)**
    (circle one)   (Millionaire card -10 or +10)   _____

8. **True or False Score   (-5 or +5)**
    (circle one)   (Millionaire card -10 or +10)   _____

9. **True or False Score   (-5 or +5)**
    (circle one)   (Millionaire card -10 or +10)   _____

10. **True or False Score   (-5 or +5)**
    (circle one)   (Millionaire card -10 or +10)   _____

11. **True or False Score   (-5 or +5)**
    (circle one)   (Millionaire card -10 or +10)   _____

12. **True or False Score   (-5 or +5)**
    (circle one)   (Millionaire card -10 or +10)   _____

13. **True or False Score   (-5 or +5)**
    (circle one)   (Millionaire card -10 or +10)   _____

14. **True or False Score   (-5 or +5)**
    (circle one)   (Millionaire card -10 or +10)   _____

15. **True or False Score   (-5 or +5)**
    (circle one)   (Millionaire card -10 or +10)   _____

NAME: _____ CLASS PERIOD: _____

A Mystery of Two Families

Part 1. The Mystery

The Robinson and Murray families are alike in several ways. They earn the same family income, live in the same neighborhood, are similar in age, and have two children each. Yet the Robinsons are much wealthier than the Murrays. Why is this?

The Robinsons spend time managing their money, and they spend less money than they earn. Mr. and Mrs. Robinson have saved $250,000, which makes for a good start on their retirement fund. They also have established savings plans to help their children with college expenses. And the Robinsons are working to improve their capacity for future income. Mr. Robinson is taking evening courses to complete an advanced degree, and Mrs. Robinson is taking weekend seminars offered at no cost by her employer. Both are hoping for promotions at work.

The Murrays are always worried about money. While their house is worth the same amount of money as the Robinsons' house, the Murrays have a larger mortgage to pay off, so they pay more in interest than the Robinsons do. They drive newer cars than the Robinsons drive, and their credit-card balances keep increasing every month. They say they do not have enough time or money to improve their education. Although they could sell their house for more than they owe on their mortgage, they have no other savings. They hope their children will get scholarships to pay for college.

In short, the Robinsons are wealthier than the Murrays because they spend less than they earn and as a result they have more assets (for example, they have large balances in their savings accounts) and fewer liabilities (the Murrays have larger mortgage-interest payments, larger credit-card balances, larger auto loans, etc.). And the gap is likely to grow as time goes on, since the Robinsons are investing in their capacity for earning by improving their education, while the Murrays are not.

Part 2. An Approach to Solving the Mystery

For a better understanding of why the Robinsons are wealthier than the Murrays, despite the similarities between the two families, let's apply some basic points of economic reasoning. Our approach to economic reasoning, summarized in The Handy Dandy Guide, is based on six main ideas.

The Handy Dandy Guide
1. People choose.

This may seem obvious, but think for a minute about how many people say, in one situation or another, that they "have no choice." In fact, we ALWAYS have a choice—though sometimes, of course, the choices can be very difficult. The Robinsons choose to spend a few hours every week managing their money. They choose to set financial goals, to have a plan for their spending, to keep track of their expenses, and to adjust their spending if they go "over budget." Their goal is to save 10 percent of their income each month. They study ways to invest their savings, comparing rates of return and risks on different savings plans or other investments. The Murrays choose not to spend time managing their money. They don't communicate much about money within the family, making most spending decisions independently. And they choose not to set spending limits. They use their two credit cards frequently; without the credit cards they would find it very difficult to manage their day-to-day purchases. They do work hard at their jobs. When they are not working they enjoy relaxing or going out to dinner.

2. All choices involve costs.

Choices come with costs. Some costs are dollar costs. If you choose to buy a computer, you must pay the purchase price. But there is another kind of cost that also attaches to choices. It is called opportunity cost. For any choice you make, your opportunity cost is your next-best option: the next-best choice you could have made but did not make. For someone who buys a computer, the opportunity cost is the next-best use she could have made of the money spent on the computer. For someone who goes to a movie, the opportunity cost is the next-best use he could have made of the time and money he spent to go to the movie.

For the Robinsons, the opportunity cost of managing their money and furthering their education is having less time to relax, less time to go out to dinner, and so on. For the Murrays, the opportunity cost of relaxing and going out to dinner is that they are not managing their money or furthering their education.

Making good choices involves comparing the benefits and costs of decisions. The Robinsons are wealthier and will continue to grow wealthier than the Murrays because of the choices they make.

3. People respond to incentives in predictable ways.

An incentive is a benefit or cost that influences a person's decision. One powerful incentive is money. Money is important because of the goods and services we can buy with it. It is also important because having money opens up the range of choices and opportunities people face. People work to earn money, but they also work to accomplish their goals and to have satisfying careers. By managing your money carefully, you can gain full benefits from your hard work, and you can position yourself, financially, to accomplish other goals.

People earn money by working for it, but it is also possible to earn money by making deposits in savings accounts and earning interest on those savings. The prospect of earning interest creates an incentive to save. It also creates an incentive for lenders; lenders earn money from the interest payments borrowers make as they pay off their loans.

One incentive encouraging the Robinsons to save is that, with savings, they will have more goods and services available to them in the future. They will also be able to achieve other goals, including helping others; and more choices will be open to them than they otherwise could have had. It is possible to think in the same way about the incentive for getting a good education. To get a good education, it is necessary to spend time, effort, and perhaps money on your studies; but the incentive for doing so is that, with a good education, you will be able to earn more income in the future, understand more about the world, and have more control over your life.

4. People create economic systems that influence choices and incentives.

The American economic system relies on markets, choices, and incentives. Americans are free to start a business, get an education, choose an occupation, and buy or not buy an incredible variety of goods and services. Americans may save or not save; they may rent an apartment or buy a house; they may buy a new car, a used car, or no car; and they may use credit cards or debit cards or pay cash for things they buy. Each one of these decisions comes with an opportunity cost. Every choice we make affects other opportunities, sometimes more than we realize. For example, the Murrays have chosen to buy newer and more expensive cars than the cars the Robinsons have bought. As a result, the Murrays also pay more for insurance, taxes, maintenance, etc. All of the expenses related to the more expensive cars add up to more money that they can't use to save for other goals, such as retirement. The Robinsons keep their cars for quite a while, and when they do replace their cars, they buy used. As a result, they keep their costs for cars and car-related expenses (insurance and taxes) down, and they therefore have more money available to save for retirement and even some fun family goals such as a vacation.

5. People gain when they trade voluntarily.

"Voluntarily" refers to doing something because you want to, not because someone forced you. Neither the Robinsons nor the Murrays are forced to buy goods and services. They are not forced to work for their employers (when you work, you trade your time and labor for money that you can use to buy goods and services). They do these things because the benefits are greater than the costs. Of course things can go wrong when people trade. If you don't gather sound information and trade carefully, you may find you don't benefit as much from the trade as you expected. The key is to determine whether the benefits will be greater than the costs. The Murrays might ask, for example, whether buying expensive cars today is a greater benefit to them than making contributions to a retirement fund and a college fund for their children.

6. People's choices have consequences for the future.

If you watch television and read newspaper and magazine advertisements, you might suppose that everyone lives for today. Most people, however, also live for tomorrow. Otherwise, why would we conserve, save, and invest? Life is not a lottery. People are affected from time to time by good luck and bad luck, but overall they shape their futures by the decisions they make—the good decisions and the bad ones. The Robinsons have acquired a measure of wealth because they save more and spend less than they earn. The Robinsons communicate within the family about their goals and spending, and this helps them to make good choices for their family. Even though the Murrays work hard, they spend as much as they earn—or more—and so they have almost no savings. They don't communicate with one another about their money; they don't set financial goals or pay much attention to their spending; and so it is hard for them to save for the future. The Robinsons' past decisions have affected their present wealth and lifestyle. For the Murrays, past and current decisions will have a great impact on their ability to live well in the future. It is important to find a balance between enjoying your money today and being able to live the way you would like to live at a later date.

Questions:

a. What is an opportunity cost?

b. Why is opportunity cost important when you make choices?

c. Why do people want to be wealthy?

d. Why do the choices we make now matter in the future?

e. What incentives encourage people to save money?

f. Why are the Robinsons wealthier than the Murrays?

NAME: _____ CLASS PERIOD: _____

The Boring School Mystery

Most high school students believe school is boring. Yet most students graduate from high school. Why do students stay in school if school is so boring? Can the Handy Dandy Guide provide the answer to this mystery?

There are many reasons to stay in school and many reasons to drop out. For each of the following reasons, put an "S" for "stay in school" or a "D" for "drop out of school." Then use the Handy Dandy Guide to explain why more people stay in school than drop out.

1. _____ High school dropouts can get a job and thus provide more financial help for their families than their friends in high school can.

2. _____ High school graduates will have higher incomes in the future than the incomes of high school dropouts.

3. _____ High school graduates are able to go on to college.

4. _____ High school students must follow school rules, which limit freedom.

5. _____ High school dropouts can work full-time and have a better car, clothes, and social life than their friends in high school.

6. _____ Parents are happy when their children graduate from high school.

7. _____ School activities, such as sports and music, are fun for many students.

8. _____ Increased knowledge opens up increased choices and opportunities.

Questions:

a. What is the cost of staying in school?

b. What is the cost of dropping out of school?

c. What incentives encourage people to stay in school?

d. How does the American economic system encourage people to graduate from high school?

e. Is going to high school voluntary, or are young people required to go to high school?

f. Why do some students choose to drop out of school?

g. Why do most students choose to stay in high school and graduate?

h. What are the future consequences of a decision to drop out of school or stay in school?

NAME: _____ CLASS PERIOD: _____

Decision Making

A fundamental lesson in economics is that there is no such thing as a free lunch. There is no such thing as a free lunch because individuals, businesses, governments, and economic systems all face scarcity. Because of scarcity, we must make choices; and the consequence of every choice is that something else is not chosen. This means that for every personal, workplace, and governmental decision there is a cost—the something else not chosen. A wise decision involves weighing the benefits and costs of the alternatives from which individuals must choose.

There is no getting around the condition of scarcity, or the choices and costs it creates. We face scarcity because our resources are limited and our economic wants are unlimited. Economic wants always outstrip the limited resources available to satisfy them. Without scarcity, it would be a different world; everything you wanted would be freely available.

People's wants are never fully satisfied. No matter what we already have, we would like to have more. The United States is one of the richest nations in the world, but poverty still exists. Even wealthy individuals desire more. Few of us are ever fully satisfied with our education, health care, and standard of living. Most everyone would like to have a higher income. Our wants are limited only by our imagination. Wants also change over time. Twenty years ago, few, if any, Americans had DVD/Blu-ray players, cell phones with cameras and video, MP3 players, car navigation systems, or digital cameras. Millions of people now own these items. Unfortunately, our resources are limited. We have only so many human resources, natural resources, and capital resources.

Human resources are the physical, intellectual, and creative talents of people. When you are working, you are using human resources. Also, when you get a better education, you are said to have improved your human capital. When people are better educated, they tend to be more productive; as a result, they usually enjoy a higher standard of living.

Natural resources are gifts of nature. They include water, forests, natural gas, oil, and climate. Natural resources are not the only resources a nation needs to become rich, but they can assist countries in improving economic outcomes.

Capital resources include those goods that are used to produce other goods and services. Tools, factories, equipment, and office buildings are examples of capital resources. In economics, the word capital refers to items used to produce something else. Capital does not refer to money.

Money is best thought of as a medium of exchange. It is used to make the buying and selling of goods and services easier. People like more money because they can use it to buy more stuff. It's the stuff that is important. Printing more money does not mean that more stuff has been produced, nor does it mean that we are all better off. Imagine how easy it would be to improve our living standards if all we had to do was print more money. None of us would have to go to work if this was all it took to be better off!

It should be clear that more money does not eliminate or even reduce scarcity. Scarcity is a fundamental condition of all economic systems. Because of scarcity, we must make choices. Every choice involves an opportunity cost. The opportunity cost of a decision is the next-best alternative that is given up. It is the value of what you give up in order to get what you want.

Questions:

a. Why is there no such thing as a free lunch?

b. Give some examples of natural resources, human resources, and capital resources.

c. What is capital?

d. Why do economists NOT view money as capital?

e. What is an opportunity cost?

NAME: _____ CLASS PERIOD: _____

Personal Decision Making

This exercise focuses on making personal decisions. Our personal resources include time, energy, and skills that we use to satisfy our wants. They also include the financial resources (such as money, savings bonds, and deposit accounts in banks) that we have accumulated over our lifetime.

We use these personal resources to purchase goods and services. Goods are things we can touch, such as cars, houses, computers, and cell phones. Services are activities such as rock concerts, education, movies, insurance, loans, vacations, and health care. Of course, we cannot have all the goods and services we want because of scarcity. But we can have more goods and services if we choose wisely. By carefully considering the costs and benefits of our decisions, we can improve our lives.

A College for Maria

Maria Delgado will graduate from high school this spring. She plans to attend college, but she does not know which college to attend. She is using a decision-making model in order to make a better choice. Let's work through Maria's decision, using the five-step decision-making model.

Step 1: Define the Problem

Maria must recognize the problem. She knows that all colleges and universities are not alike, and she must choose the one that is right for her. She plans to major in marketing.

Step 2: List the Alternatives

Maria has found three main alternatives. State U is a big university with 30,000 students, and it offers both undergraduate and graduate programs. Many undergraduate classes are very large; some have more than 300 students. The tuition is reasonable. The business school and the marketing program are highly ranked nationally. State U is located 150 miles from Maria's hometown.

Local Community College is a two-year college only a few miles away from Maria's house. Its classes are smaller than State U's, averaging about 40 students. There are marketing classes. While some faculty members are outstanding, Maria has heard that most do not have Ph.D. degrees (most faculty members at State U do have Ph.D. degrees). The tuition for LCC is low, and if she decides on LCC, Maria could keep her part-time job.

Private College, which has only 3,000 students, is located 200 miles from Maria's hometown in a neighboring state. The classes are small, and the students get a lot of individual attention and help. The college offers marketing courses. Its admission standards are high, but Maria is an outstanding student and thinks she has a good chance of being accepted. Tuition is expensive. Private College gives scholarships and loans, but the cost would still be higher than the cost at State U.

STEP 3: Identify Your Criteria

For any choice, your criteria are important considerations by which the alternative possibilities may be judged. People often differ in the criteria they consider important in making choices.

Maria's most important criteria are these:
- Low-cost tuition, because her family is not wealthy.
- High-quality education, particularly in marketing.
- Small class size and personal attention.
- Close location to home, because she feels she would miss her friends if she were far away.

Step 4: Evaluate Your Alternatives

Maria must now evaluate her alternatives against her criteria.   She has decided to use the decision-making grid shown at the end of this exercise. She will use a "+" and "-" system to evaluate each alternative. One plus sign is positive and two plus signs are even better—very positive. A minus sign is negative. Two minus signs are very negative. Complete the grid before going to Step 5.

Step 5: Make a Decision

Maria decided to attend Local Community College for two years. Cost is very important to her. By attending the community college while working part-time, she might even be able to save some money. She felt the private college had the best program for her, but it is too expensive and too far from home. The community college had the most pluses. Low cost and closeness to home were very important to Maria, and the community college ranked highest on these criteria.

A longer-term option for Maria may be to save money and apply for scholarships during the two years when she attends the community college. If she does this, she may be able to attend the private school for her final two years of college.

Maria's Decision-Making Grid

Based on the information in this exercise, use the grid to help Maria make a decision. Then answer the questions that follow.

What is the problem?

Fill in the boxes with "+", "++", or "-", "--", as you think Maria might have decided.

ALTERNATIVES	CRITERIA			
	Low Cost	Quality Programs	Personal Attention	Close to Home
State U				
Local Community College				
Private College				

Maria's Decision _____

Questions:

a. Why is the decision-making model important?

b. Are there any additional criteria that Maria did not consider that you feel are important in choosing a college?

c. Do you agree with Maria's choice? Why or why not?

NAME: _____ CLASS PERIOD: _____

Buying a New Computer or Digital Camera

You can use the decision-making model and grid for any consumer decision. Assume you want to buy a computer or a digital camera. Fill out the decision-making grid that follows and decide which computer or digital camera to buy. Find the alternative models at electronics superstores, computer or camera stores, or online stores. Develop your criteria, which could include size, cost, memory, disk capacity, speed, audio and video capabilities, etc. Choose the criteria that are most important to you; fill out the grid; make a choice; and justify it.

Decision-Making Grid

The Problem:

Criteria ➡ / ⬇ Alternatives					

The Decision:

Introduction

Earning Income

How much have you thought about what occupation you will seek after leaving school? Not much? That is not unusual. Even if you are among the few who have a plan, you will probably reexamine this plan several times over the coming months and years.

Finding a job is important. Many high school students have part-time jobs, and they may be familiar with the process of finding a job. However, finding a job after technical school or college is different from finding a part-time job while you are still in high school. The usual process for finding a full-time job includes writing a letter of application, preparing a resume, completing a job application, and crossing your fingers, hoping that you will be offered a job interview.

But what sort of occupation is right for you? There are abundant sources of information about various occupations and job openings. The *Occupational Outlook Handbook* in your school library or at www.bls.gov/OCO/ is a great source of information about salaries and job requirements. Similarly, there are many places to look for lists of job openings—from your local newspaper to websites on the Internet.

Ever notice how people in some occupations earn more money than people in other occupations? Ever wonder why some people are wealthier than others? Michael Dell of Dell Computers is worth billions. Google founders Larry Page and Sergey Brin are also worth billions. On the other hand, people who manage gourmet coffee shops earn a whole lot less and are much less wealthy. Why is that? One explanation has to do with the risks that entrepreneurs like Dell, Page, and Brin take when they start their own business. We all know that risks don't always pay off. But, when they do, they can lead to increased wealth.

Another way to become wealthier has to do with an individual's level of education. Economists call education and training "human capital." On average, people who have higher levels of education earn more, sometimes significantly more, than those with lower levels of education. For example, people who graduate from high school earn more than those who do not. People who complete at least some years of college usually earn more than people who never go to college. Because of this, the time and money you spend on your education should be looked upon as an investment in your human capital. Investing time and money in your education may well provide you with good returns in the form of higher income over many years.

If you have held a part-time job, you may have had a rude surprise when you received your first paycheck. You might have figured that the amount of your paycheck would simply be the total of the number of hours worked multiplied by your hourly rate of pay. But of course paychecks come with various deductions from the gross pay amount. Some of these deductions are optional, but many are mandatory. Optional deductions might include contributions to employee-paid benefits, such as a company retirement plan. Mandatory deductions include payments for income taxes and Social Security. Uncle Sam takes a bite!

NAME: _____ CLASS PERIOD: _____

The Job Application Process

Employers in recent years have been experimenting with new ways to attract employees. But most employers still tend to follow similar procedures for recruiting and hiring new workers. People who are familiar with these procedures have advantages in the job-seeking process. A good job-application process can involve as many as six steps. These steps are all very important in finding a job.

STEP 1: Looking for Job Openings

There are several sources of information about job opportunities. One important source to consider is CareerOneStop: www.careeronestop.org/. It is the most extensive service available. CareerOneStop is sponsored by the U.S Department of Labor in partnership with state-operated employment services. It is a computerized network that links state employment-services offices to provide job seekers with a pool of active job opportunities. Job seekers can search for job openings and submit resumes for employers to examine. Job seekers may research jobs within 25 miles of their homes, within counties, states, and throughout the United States. The job openings and resumes found in CareerOneStop are available on the Internet in many public libraries, colleges, universities, high schools, shopping malls, transition offices on military bases, and elsewhere. Some other Internet job sites include Monster.com and Careerbuilder.com.

Individuals increasingly are using networking as a less formal way of finding out about career opportunities. How might you uncover job opportunities using your personal network? Consider communicating by telephone or e-mail with friends and family members who, in turn, might be able to connect you to a potential employer. Consider business networking sites like LinkedIn.com. Make efforts to contact people who might know other people. Contact organizations that might help. For example, local employers may be members of a local Chamber of Commerce. These employers are often seeking new workers. Your local Chamber of Commerce will usually have information about how you can contact local employers through formal and informal channels. Other networking ideas include joining organizations and clubs, attending business luncheon meetings, and taking classes or seminars where you might come into contact with potential employers.

There are many other sources of information about jobs. Teachers and guidance counselors may know of local sources of employment. Many high schools offer co-operative or work-experience programs. Most post-secondary education institutions, such as technical schools, colleges, and universities, have career placement offices. These offices often post job openings; they may also offer workshops on job-seeking skills and may arrange for recruiters to interview students on campus.

Many communities have public and private employment agencies whose business is to help you find jobs for which you are qualified.

Don't forget to check out the classified "Help Wanted" notices in your local newspaper.

Finally, businesses and government organizations often circulate job openings. These job openings might be posted on bulletin boards which you can read by visiting the employment office of the business or government organization.

STEP 2: The Letter of Application

Job applicants often send a letter of application and a resume to a potential employer. The letter of application introduces you to the employer and allows you to tell the employer what you have to offer. A letter of application includes the normal characteristics of a business letter (typed, centered on page, and standard English). A typical letter expresses your interest in a particular job, links your experience, interest, or training to the job, and explains how you can be reached for an interview.

STEP 3: The Resume

A resume is a summary of your work-related experiences. It presents your name, telephone number, street address, e-mail address, career objective, education, GPA, work experience, abilities, and other information, such as awards, extracurricular activities (club, sports, etc.), offices held in organizations, and any special interests. Make sure your e-mail address is your name or a professional alias rather than a funny, cute, or inappropriate alias. A resume should give the employer a sense of who you are in a neat, concise, and accurate way. If you wish, you can list references (names and addresses) on the resume. References are people who can tell a prospective employer about your work habits, character, and skills. Be sure to ask permission before listing someone as a reference.

STEP 4: The Application

Employers ordinarily ask you to complete an employment application when you inquire about a job. When possible, you should type the application and return it to the employer. Note that many firms now allow you to fill out your application online. Many times, however, employers want you to complete the information on the spot. In this case, here are a few tips:

✔ Be sure to bring basic information such as your Social Security number, driver's license, and copies of necessary licenses or permits. Also, be sure to bring your resume and, if possible, a school transcript.

✔ Print clearly in the spaces provided. Use a good quality black or blue pen.

✔ Fill in all the blanks on the form. Write N/A for not available or does not apply, when appropriate, so the employer knows that you did not skip parts of the form.

✔ Be truthful. Give complete answers.

✔ Be sure there is no personal or inappropriate information on your social networking pages (e.g. Facebook). Potential employers are checking these sites for information about you.

STEP 5: The Interview

It is typical for an interested employer to contact you and arrange for a job interview. The job interview is a procedure in which you may be questioned about the statements you made in your application. The interview also allows the employer to gather other job-related information from you. Here are a few tips to consider as you prepare for a job interview:

✔ Find out detailed information about the company or agency. Often, companies have Internet sites or brochures that provide information on their mission and organization.

✔ Make a list of questions to ask about information that you want to obtain, such as work schedules, benefits, and pay.

✔ Arrive on time or a little early. Never be late. Go alone.

✔ Be neat and clean. Dress modestly and conservatively.

✔ Use minimal jewelry or fragrance.

✔ Do not smoke or chew gum.

✔ Be poised and confident. It is normal to be nervous, but try your best to appear relaxed.

✔ Do not appear overconfident or arrogant.

✔ Greet the interviewer with a firm handshake.

✔ Establish eye contact.

✔ Concentrate on clear communication. Speak clearly. Avoid slang or improper language. Listen carefully. Don't interrupt. Be responsive and truthful.

✔ Be ready for some open-ended questions. "Tell me about your qualifications for this job" or "Describe the ideal candidate for this position" are two possibilities.

✔ Emphasize your strong points. Be ready to be asked about your strengths as well as weaknesses.

✔ Be positive, upbeat, and enthusiastic.

STEP 6: The Thank-You Letter

Make sure you follow up with a letter thanking the person/people who interviewed you. Let them know you appreciated their time, and you look forward to hearing from them. In a thank-you letter you can also re-emphasize any skills, strengths, or other qualities you possess that are important to the position. And you can convey additional information you forgot to mention, or address any concerns that were brought up, during the interview.

Questions:

a. What are the six primary steps in the job application process?

b. What are two suggestions for finding a job?

c. What are two tips for writing a letter of application?

d. What information is ordinarily included on a resume?

e. There are many suggestions for how best to conduct yourself during a job interview. Which ones do you think are the most important, and why?

f. Why is it important to send a follow-up thank-you letter?

NAME: _____ CLASS PERIOD: _____

Sample Job Application

Below is a typical job application. Examine it to see how easy it would be for you to complete the application today. Answer the questions found after the form.

JOB APPLICATION

Today's date _____

PERSONAL INFORMATION (please print clearly)

Name _____ Tel. # ( ) _____
       Last   First   Middle   Area Code

Email address _____

Address _____
       City   State   Zip

Date of birth _____ Social Security No. _____

Are you employed now? ☐ Yes ☐ No

If yes, where? _____

In case of emergency notify:

Name _____ Tel. # ( ) _____
       Last   First   Middle   Area Code

Address _____
       City   State   Zip

AVAILABILITY

Are you legally able to be employed in the U.S. ? ☐ Yes ☐ No

What type of position are you seeking? ☐ Part-time ☐ Full-time

          M   T   W   T   F   S   S

Hours   From _____

Available   To _____

How will you get to work? _____

continued on page 2

EDUCATION

School name and location _____

Total # years attended _____ Did you graduate? _____ GPA _____

Degree, major or total hours _____

High school _____ ☐Yes ☐No

Trade or business school _____ ☐ Yes ☐No

College/university _____ ☐Yes ☐No

EMPLOYMENT HISTORY

1. Company _____

Address _____ Tel. # (   ) _____
          City   State   Zip

Position _____ Supervisor _____

Dates worked from _____ To _____

Wage _____ Reason for leaving _____

2. Company _____

Address _____ Tel. # (   ) _____
          City   State   Zip

Position _____ Supervisor _____

Dates worked from _____ To _____

Wage _____ Reason for leaving _____

SKILLS *(Complete if applying for clerical, secretarial or data processing position.)*

Keyboarding ☐ Yes ___WPM ☐ No   Word processing ☐Yes ___WPM ☐No

Spreadsheets ☐Yes ☐No   Data entry ☐Yes ☐No

Desktop publishing ☐Yes ☐No   Internet experience ☐Yes ☐No

Word processing software *(specify)*

_____

Spreadsheet Software *(specify)*

_____

Continued on page 3

List other skills, professional certifications, or training which you feel qualify you for the position for which you are applying.

_____

REFERENCES *(other than relatives)*

Name _____ Occupation _____ Tel. # (   ) _____

Address _____

                                                  City   State   Zip

Name _____ Occupation _____ Tel. # (   ) _____

Address _____

                                                  City   State   Zip

Name _____ Occupation _____ Tel. # (   ) _____

Address _____

                                                  City   State   Zip

SIGNATURE

I declare the information provided by me in this application is true, correct, and complete to the best of my knowledge. I understand that if employed, any falsification, misstatement, or omission in connection to my application, whether on this document or not, may result in immediate termination of employment.

I authorize the references listed above to give you any and all information concerning my previous or current employment and any pertinent information they may have, personal or otherwise, and release all parties from all liability for any damage that may result from furnishing the same to you.

I acknowledge that employment may be conditional upon successful completion of a substance-abuse screening test as part of the company's pre-employment policy.

I understand it is unlawful to require or administer a lie detector test as a condition of employment or continued employment. An employer who violates this law shall be subject to criminal and/or civil liabilities.

_____   _____

           Applicant Signature   Date

Americans with Disabilities

Most of the information provided by potential employees to potential employers is routine and job-related. However, Title I of the Americans with Disabilities Act requires that individuals with disabilities make known to employers that they need special accommodations (such as a Braille cash register or a desk that has wheelchair access), in order to do the tasks that are required for the job. To the best of their ability, employers are to make these accommodations for applicants who meet all other job requirements.

Information Rights

The vast majority of prospective employers only want to learn how your background and skills match their job requirements. However, some employers may stray into asking about non-job-related information. Some areas of information are off-limits for the job application and the job interview. With rare exceptions, federal law prohibits hiring decisions being made on the basis of race, color, national origin, religion, gender, pregnancy, marital status, parenthood, age, height, weight, criminal record, or perceived disability. Interviewers and job applications are not allowed to pose personal questions that do not pertain to the requirements of the job. If such questions are asked, you should politely decline to answer. Also note that potential employers may run your credit report as part of your application process and often attempt to assess your character by investigating your online identity as well.

Questions:

a. What information is requested on the job application?

b. What are the obligations of individuals with disabilities?

c. What sort of questions are employers not supposed to ask?

NAME: _____ CLASS PERIOD: _____

Job Postings

WE ARE SEEKING DEPENDABLE INDIVIDUALS WHO CAN GROW WITH OUR COMPANY. WE OFFER FULL-TIME AND PART-TIME POSITIONS WITH A VARIETY OF SHIFTS AND SCHEDULES. PREVIOUS EXPERIENCE WITH THESE JOBS WILL BE HELPFUL.

ADMINISTRATIVE ASSISTANT

Supports managers by answering phones, typing correspondence, and coordinating travel schedules and meetings. Must be able to handle a variety of tasks under deadline. Skills required include word processing and attention to detail.

CASHIER

Conducts customer transactions with speed, accuracy, and efficiency while meeting or exceeding service quality standards. Accepts express transactions from clients, such as deposits, withdrawals, transfers, and checks to be cashed. Sets up, closes, and balances cash at work station. Bilingual skills a plus.

DATA ENTRY OPERATOR

Posts transactions to online computer system. Creates specific reports as requested. Skills required include accurate 10-key data entry and typing.

LINE AND PREP COOK Responsible
for preparing quality food in fast-paced kitchen. Skills: Ability to follow exacting preparation standards; teamwork with other kitchen and wait staff to provide high-quality food and service to customers.

MACHINE OPERATOR

Operates statement-rendering machine. Does minor repair work on machine. Skills: Must have good mechanical aptitude and be able to lift 10-20 pounds.

RESEARCH CLERK

Carries out interdepartmental research. Reconciles a general ledger accounting system to a variety of sources. Determines charges to customers for research inquiries. Verifies errors and makes adjustments. Good verbal and written skills are a must, along with the ability to learn quickly and follow directions. Skills required include accounting, calculator, and personal computer.

WAREHOUSE DRIVER

Responsible for delivering orders. Must have good personality for customer interaction, strong driving record, and knowledge of city and suburbs.

WE OFFER COMPETITIVE SALARIES AND A COMPREHENSIVE BENEFITS PACKAGE, INCLUDING MEDICAL/DENTAL, LIFE INSURANCE, RETIREMENT PLANS, CHILD CARE ASSISTANCE, AND PAID VACATIONS AND HOLIDAYS.
WE ARE AN EQUAL OPPORTUNITY EMPLOYER.

Interviewer Evaluation Form

Name of applicant: _____

Interviewed by: _____

Position applied for: _____

SAMPLE INTERVIEW QUESTIONS

- Why are you applying for this job?
- What about the job most appeals to you?
- What about the job, if anything, does not appeal to you?
- What are your qualifications for this position?
- What experiences do you have that will be helpful to you in this job?
- What are your strengths?
- What are your weaknesses?
- What would you like to be doing five years from now, and how do you think this job can help you get there?
- Is there anything else I should know about you in considering you for this position?

INTERVIEWER'S EVALUATION

The job applicant: (check all that apply)

- ☐ Seemed prepared for the interview
- ☐ Appeared confident
- ☐ Communicated clearly
- ☐ Was able to relate strengths and/or experiences to job needs
- ☐ Asked relevant questions

The job application: (check all that apply)

- ☐ Was neatly prepared and presented
- ☐ Was thorough
- ☐ Did a good job of highlighting the candidate's strengths and skills

The things that most impress me about this job applicant are:

The areas in which this candidate might improve are:

NAME: _____ CLASS PERIOD: _____

Take the Test

Complete the questionnaire below. Read each statement on the left and place an X in the column that reflects whether you agree or disagree with the statement and how strongly you agree or disagree. There are no right or wrong answers.

Statement	1 Strongly Disagree	2 Disagree	3 Agree	4 Strongly Agree
1. I sometimes enjoy taking risks.				
2. I like to work hard at projects that interest me.				
3. I have a high level of energy.				
4. I want to achieve results based largely on my own efforts.				
5. I like being creative.				
6. I like to start projects on my own.				
7. I tend to see tasks through to completion.				
8. I am confident in my abilities.				
9. I am good at a lot of different tasks.				
10. I am interested in making lots of money.				
Totals				

Total Points = _____

When you have completed the questionnaire, notice that each response has a numeric rating. Add the total number of points of the ratings you have given each statement and write the total in the space below the questionnaire.

NAME: _____ CLASS PERIOD: _____

Who Are Entrepreneurs?

Most people work for others. Working for others, however, is not for everyone. Some individuals welcome the challenge of starting their own business and working for themselves. Research on entrepreneurs suggests that they share certain characteristics. Entrepreneurs tend to be willing to take risks, be independent, lead, and to enjoy being recognized. Among other things, entrepreneurs tend to be confident, hard working, well organized, and self-starters.

Condition of Employment	Work for Someone Else	Work for Yourself
Job Stability	Job stability depends largely on the success of the division, department, or immediate superiors.	Job stability depends almost completely on your success and that of the business.
Work Hours	Full time work varies from 40 hours per week to fairly long hours depending on job and salary.	Very long hours but self-directed.
Personal Success	Your success depends largely on the success of the company, department, or superiors.	Your personal success depends almost completely on you and the success of the business.
Salary	Usually set in a pre-determined range for the department or position reflecting market conditions for the job. Raises are often given after predictable periods of time.	Low in the beginning. Entrepreneurs often take little salary in the beginning so that most income can be put back into the business. Earnings depend on the success of the business.
Benefits	A standard package of benefits is often provided. Benefits often include major medical insurance and perhaps other coverage. Paid vacations, personal and sick days are often included. Some type of retirement program such as a 401k program is often available.	Benefits depend on what you are willing and able to provide as the owner of the business. Vacations tend to be rare and generally mean lost income.
Job Responsibilities	Responsibilities are often explained in an employee handbook but may change as conditions in the company change.	Entrepreneurs must be prepared to do everything. Bookkeeping, selling, cleaning, painting, and producing items are likely to be included.

Questions:

a. What are some of the characteristics of entrepreneurs?

b. Name at least three important elements of working for someone else.

c. Name at least three important elements of working for yourself.

d. What is best for you? Working for someone else or working for yourself?

e. Identify some entrepreneurs in your community, preferably ones that you know personally. How might they be able to help you if you decided to become an entrepreneur?

NAME: _____ CLASS PERIOD: _____

I Wonder Why Nobody Ever Made a … ?

Describe a good or service you think consumers want. It might be something that exists now, provided in a new way. Or your idea might be an original idea for an entirely new good or service.

Which types of consumers do you think might be interested in this good or service? Identify your customers.

How would you produce the good or service you have in mind?

How many people would you need to hire to get started? What might their jobs be?

Where might you find money to start up your new business? Personal savings? Loans from friends or family? Bank loans?

Develop a one-minute commercial for your good or service. You might wish to design a sign, write a jingle, or create a slogan that would catch the attention of customers and encourage them to buy your good or service.

NAME: _____ CLASS PERIOD: _____

Why Some Jobs Pay More Than Others

**Read the following material, and study the table on the next page.
Then answer the questions at the end of the exercise.**

The money a person receives in exchange for work or use of property is called income. Income can come from many sources. People possess certain assets that they can use to generate income. These assets may include savings, stocks, land, and rental property. However, most of the income people earn in the United States comes from the work they do. Wages and other income from labor make up about 70 percent of every dollar of total income. The rest (approximately 30 percent) comes from interest, rents, and profits, including the income earned by entrepreneurs.

Not everyone makes the same amount of income. *Forbes* Magazine reported that top celebrity earners for 2009 included Oprah Winfrey, with earnings of $315 million; U2, at $130 million; Tiger Woods, at $105 million; Beyonce Knowles, at $87 million; Sandra Bullock, at $56 million; Kobe Bryant, at $48 million; David Beckham, at $44 million; and Maria Sharapova, at $25 million. The Bureau of Labor Statistics reports that the 2008 median annual earning figure for dentists was $142,810; for registered nurses, $62,450; for special education teachers, $50,020; for secretary/administrative assistant (non-legal, medical or executive), $29,050; and for full-time cosmetologists, $26,712, excluding tips.

What causes income to vary so much from one occupation to another?

One factor is the market for different occupations. At least in the near future, for example, demand for dental hygienists is expected to grow much faster than average for all occupations, owing in part to increasing demand for dental care. This change in demand will probably cause wages for dental hygienists to go up. In contrast, demand for radio and television announcers is expected to decline. This change in demand will probably cause wages for announcers to go down.

Other factors also contribute to differences in earnings. People with more natural ability in their occupation tend to make more money than those with less ability. People who work hard typically make more money than others who don't. People who get along with others and are self-disciplined tend to earn more money than people who are hard to get along with or are less disciplined.

Another important factor related to income is **human capital**. Human capital is the set of intangible assets individuals bring to their work: Their knowledge, skills, talent, even their health. All these factors have a bearing on income; workers who bring a rich stock of human capital to their work typically do well. One good measure of human capital is education. There are notable exceptions, of course, but workers with more education tend to earn more income than workers with less education. One way to increase income, therefore, is to **invest** in one's own human capital, especially by getting more education. Gary Becker, recipient of the 1992

Nobel Memorial Prize in Economic Science, has explained that, on average, completing high school and earning a college degree will raise a person's income even after accounting for the **direct costs** (e.g., tuition and books) and the **indirect costs** (e.g., income that an individual could otherwise have earned during time spent in school) of getting an education. The gains in income occur because investment in human capital typically leads to increased worker productivity. Since workers with higher levels of productivity typically earn higher incomes, the return from investing in human capital can make a big difference in one's earnings.

The U.S. Census Bureau reports on the relationship between levels of formal education and income. Please examine the table below and respond to the questions that follow.

Level of Formal Education and Income	
Level of Education	**Average Median Income of Males and Females Aged 25 and Over, 2008**
Less than 9th grade	$18,180
9th grade to 12th grade, no diploma	$20,246
High school graduate (includes GED)	$27,963
Some college, no degree	$31,947
Associate's degree	$36,399
Bachelor's degree	$48,097
Master's degree	$58,522
Professional degree	$87,775
Doctoral degree	$80,776

Source: U.S. Census Bureau, Pinc-03 Educational attainment—people 25 years old and over, by total money earnings in 2008.

Questions:

a. What is income?

b. What factors other than education contribute to increased income from work?

c. What is human capital?

d. Examine the table in this exercise. Describe the relationship between education and income from work. Does education pay?

e. In 2008, how much more would a high school graduate expect to earn per year, compared to an 11th-grade dropout?

f. Assuming a 40-year work life and no pay increases, how much more might a high school graduate expect to earn over a lifetime, compared to an 11th-grade dropout?

g. Does it pay to stay in school one more year and graduate? Why?

h. In 2008, how much more would a college graduate expect to earn per year, compared to a high school graduate?

i. Assuming a 40-year work life and no pay increases, how much more might a college graduate expect to earn over a lifetime, compared to a high school graduate?

j. Is education a good investment?

NAME: _____ CLASS PERIOD: _____

Education and Training

What level of education and/or training is likely to be required in the future in order to access the fastest-growing jobs? It is hard to predict, but the U.S. Bureau of Labor Statistics (BLS) provides useful information about how job markets are changing. The Bureau reports that the fastest-growing jobs will require some education beyond high school. In general, jobs that require more education are expected to grow more rapidly than those that require on-the-job training.

Study the chart below. Answer the questions following the chart after you have read and analyzed the information it presents.

Percent change in employment, by education or training category, 2008-18 (projected)

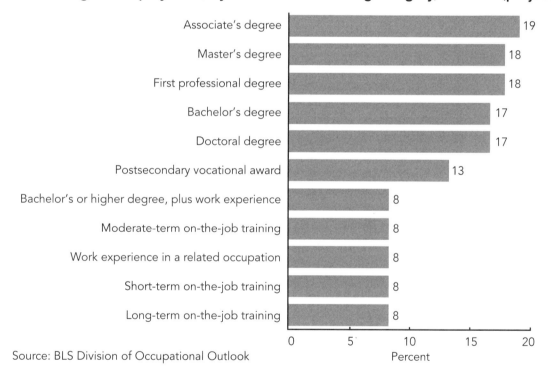

Source: BLS Division of Occupational Outlook

Questions:

a. What three levels of education or formal education and training are associated with the fastest-growing jobs?

b. What levels of education or training are associated with slower-growing jobs?

NAME: _____ CLASS PERIOD: _____

What Are All These Deductions from My Paycheck?

It's exciting to receive your first paycheck. But for many young people, that first rush of excitement soon yields to disappointment. They quickly realize the money they earned is not the same as the money they received. Uncle Sam and a lot of others have taken a bite out of that paycheck.

GROSS PAY

Gross pay is the total amount of money a worker earns before any deductions are made. For example, many employees are paid at an hourly rate. In the case of an hourly employee, the record of hours worked is multiplied by the employee's hourly rate of pay. This results in the employee's gross pay.

40 hours x $10 an hour = $400

Gross pay = $400

Similar calculations are made to determine the gross pay of employees who receive a bi-weekly, monthly, or an annual salary.

NET PAY

The amount left after all deductions are taken out of the gross pay is the net pay. This is the actual amount of an employee's paycheck. Net pay is often called take-home pay because it is the amount of money an employee actually receives on payday.

Gross pay
- Deductions
= Net pay

REQUIRED (MANDATORY) DEDUCTIONS

Federal income tax, state income tax, local taxes, and FICA are among the required deductions taken from an employee's paycheck. FICA is the abbreviation for the Federal Insurance Contributions Act. FICA provides for a federal system of old-age, survivors, disability, and hospital insurance. The old-age, survivors, and disability portion is paid by the Social Security tax. The hospital insurance portion is paid by the Medicare tax. The actual amount deducted from a paycheck for federal, state, and local income taxes is determined by reference to tax tables provided by the various levels of government.

Employers use the information provided by the tax tables and combine it with information from employees to determine how much to take out of an employee's paycheck. Employees complete the W-4 Form (Employee's Withholding Allowance Certificate) when they are hired. This form tells the employer the number of allowances the employee wishes to claim. For example, an employee is able to claim allowances for himself or herself, a spouse, and children under 21 years of age whom the employee supports. The more allowances an employee claims, the less money withheld from the employee's paycheck.

Mandatory Deductions From Your Paycheck		
Deduction	**What do you get?**	**Who pays?**
Federal income tax	This tax helps pay for services provided by the federal government, such as defense, human services, and the monitoring and regulation of trade.	Employee
State income tax	This tax helps pay for services provided by state government, such as roads, safety, and health. (Not all states levy an income tax.)	Employee
Local income tax	This tax helps pay for services provided by the city or other local government, such as schools, police, and fire protection. (Very few local areas levy an income tax.)	Employee
FICA: Social Security tax	This tax provides for old-age, survivors, and disability insurance.	Employee and employer
FICA: Medicare tax	This tax provides for hospital insurance for the elderly.	Employee and employer

In addition to required deductions, employers may take money directly out of employees' paychecks to pay for various employee benefits. Benefits vary by industry, by business, and by the status of the employee in the firm. Benefits may include such things as life insurance, disability insurance, medical insurance, dental insurance, retirement savings plans, and profit-sharing.

Other Deductions

Deduction	What do you get?	Who pays?
Life Insurance	Pays a beneficiary in the event that an employee dies.	Employer or employee, or shared
Long-term disability insurance	Provides benefits in the event that an employee is completely disabled.	Employer or employee, or shared
Medical insurance	Provides employee and family insurance coverage for medical care expenses including hospitalization, physician services, surgery, and major medical expenses.	Employer or employee, or shared
Dental insurance	Provides employee and family insurance coverage for dental care expenses, including preventive diagnostic, basic, major, and orthodontic services.	Employer or employee, or shared
Retirement savings plan	A tax-deferred savings plan for retirement.	Employer or employee (Employer may match percentage.)
Charity	A donation to a specific charity.	Employee (Employer may match a percentage of employee contribution.)

Questions:

a. What is gross pay?

b. What is net pay?

c. Is the amount of money shown on your paycheck equal to the total of the number of hours worked times the rate of pay?

d. Name at least three mandatory deductions that are taken out of gross pay.

e. Name three other deductions.

NAME: _____ CLASS PERIOD: _____

Tax-Saving Strategies

The U.S. income tax is progressive. The more income we earn, the higher the marginal tax rate. There are a number of ways to reduce the tax owed. One way to reduce taxable income is by deducting the cost of benefits such as insurance and retirement savings from gross income, taking advantage of favorable tax treatment the law provides for these benefits. These optional deductions reduce taxable income. With taxable income reduced, fewer taxes are owed. To calculate the tax savings of using pre-tax dollars to pay for benefits, multiply the amount spent times the marginal tax rate.

The table below shows the marginal tax rate for different levels of income. Notice that the entire paycheck is not taxed at the same rate. In fact, some income is not taxed at all!

For example, Tom is a single person who earned $20,000 in 2008. He filed Form 1040EZ to report his federal income tax. As a single taxpayer, he is allowed to deduct $8,950 of his earnings in calculating his taxable income. After subtracting $8,950 from his gross income, his taxable income was $11,050. He paid no tax on $8,950 of his income, a sum of his personal exemption ($3,500) and the standard deduction ($5,450). He then paid 10 percent on the next $8,025 ($802.50) and 15 percent tax on the last $3,025 ($453.75). So, on an income of $20,000, Tom owes approximately $1,256 in federal income taxes, and his marginal tax rate is 15 percent (this is his highest rate of tax).

What's Your Bracket?	
Taxable income range	**Marginal tax rate**
First $8,025	10%
Between $8,025 and 32,550	15%
Between $32,550 and 78,850	25%
Between $78,850 and $164,550	28%
Between $164,550 and $357,700	33%
Over $357,700	35%

Mike and Ann's Tax Strategies

Paying for Benefits with Pre-tax Dollars

It is important to know about tax-saving strategies so that you will be prepared to take advantage of them. Many people are aware of pre-tax retirement savings plans like 401ks, but they may not be as familiar with other tax strategies. Paying for health insurance, medical care, and dependent care expenses with pre-tax dollars will reduce your gross taxable income and your tax liability. Check with your employer to see if you can have these expenses deducted from your paycheck.

Retirement Savings (401k Plan). Mike and Ann are each employed by FooFoo Gourmet Coffee Shop. FooFoo offers a 401k retirement savings plan. FooFoo will match up to half of the employee's retirement contribution up to 6 percent of the employee's income. Mike contributes $1,000 and his company matches it with $500. Because Mike is in the 15 percent marginal tax bracket, this contribution saves Mike $150 in income taxes each year ($1,000 x .15 = $150). In addition, his savings are allowed to grow tax-free until he takes them out. And another bonus! FooFoo matches his retirement savings with an additional $500.

Premium Conversion Plans (Cafeteria Plans). Some employers offer a premium conversion plan (PCP) that allows you to pay your health insurance premiums with before-tax dollars. Under a PCP, the amount you pay in health insurance premiums, dependent care, and medical expenses reduces your gross taxable income dollar for dollar. For example: FooFoo Gourmet Coffee Shop offers a PCP; Mike participates, but Ann does not. Mike pays $150 per month for health insurance; but because he decided to participate in the PCP, Mike's annual gross taxable income is reduced by the $1,800 he pays in premiums.

Questions:

a. What is Mike's marginal tax rate? What does this mean?

b. How much does Mike save in taxes by paying for his health insurance with pre-tax dollars? Enter this amount into the table below by adding it to the $150 already saved from his retirement plan deductions for his Total Tax Savings.

c. What is Mike's taxable income? Enter it in the table below.

d. How much does Mike save in taxes by using pre-tax dollars to save for retirement and pay for his health insurance?

e. What are some things Mike could do with his tax savings?

f. How much tax was owed on the first $5,000 of gross income?

g. Compare Mike's gross income to Ann's gross income. What do you notice?

h. Compare Mike's taxable income to Ann's taxable income. What do you notice? Explain.

	Mike's Taxable Income	Ann's Taxable Income
Gross income	$30,000	$30,000
Less personal exemption	$3,500	$3,500
Less standard deduction	$5,450	$5,450
Less 401K contribution	$1,000	
Less health insurance pre-mium	$1,800	
Taxable income		$21,050
Total tax savings	$150 +	$0

NAME: _____ CLASS PERIOD: _____

Is It Better to Get a Tax Refund or to Have Fewer Taxes Withheld? Part 1

According to the IRS, approximately four-fifths of the people who filed taxes in 2008 received a refund. The average refund in 2008 was $2,429. While a refund of this amount sounds great to most people, think about the costs and benefits of getting a tax refund. Some taxpayers see their refund as a forced savings plan. They use the money for high-priced purchases or vacations. However, the IRS doesn't pay interest on the money it withholds. So what are you giving up to get a refund?

Instead of getting a refund, what if you had fewer taxes withheld from your paycheck and then saved the extra cash in an interest-earning bank account? The refund sum of $2,429 represents about $200 a month. With monthly deposits into a money market account earning interest at 3 percent, you could earn about $40 in interest on that sum during the course of a year.

If you are considering paying off debt with the amount that is no longer being withheld from your paycheck, it could make a big difference if you were to use the extra $200 each month to pay down your credit card debt. Assuming you have a balance of $5,000 on a credit card that charges 18 percent interest, and you currently are making monthly payments of $100, it will take you almost 8 years and $4,311 in interest to pay off your debt. However, if you increase your monthly payments to $300, you will pay off your debt in less than two years, and it will cost approximately $800 in interest—a savings of about $3,500!

Key information from Jack's recent pay stub is found on the next page. His W-2 Wage and Tax Statement is also provided. Use the information from these two sources to answer the following questions.

a. What is the difference between Jack's weekly gross pay and his net pay?

b. How many withholding allowances did Jack claim?

Jack's Pay Stub

Pay Check		Calculations Based on	
Weekly Gross Pay	$400.00	Tax Year	2008
Federal Withholding	$36.19	Gross Pay	$400.00
Social Security	$24.80	Pay Frequency	Weekly
Medicare	$5.80	Federal Filing Status	Single
Missouri Withholding	$11.00	# of Federal Allowances	0
Net Pay	$322.21	Additional Federal W/H	$0.00
		State	Missouri
		Filing Status	Single

Jack's W-2

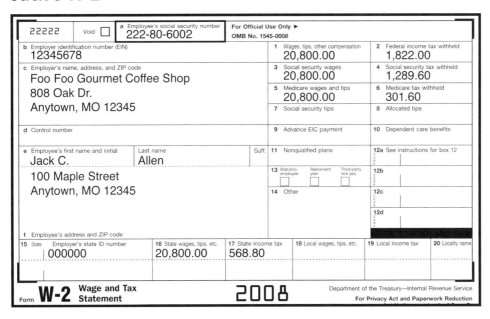

Now use Jack's W-2 statement and the tax table in Illustration 7.1 to complete Form1040EZ for Jack. When you have completed this, answer the following questions:

c. What is Jack's marginal tax rate?

d. Does Jack owe taxes or get a refund?

e. How would you recommend that Jack change his withholding allowances for next year?

Jack's Form 1040EZ

Form **1040EZ**	Department of the Treasury—Internal Revenue Service **Income Tax Return for Single and Joint Filers With No Dependents** (99) **2008**		OMB No. 1545-0074

Label (See page 9.)

Use the IRS label.

Otherwise, please print or type.

Presidential Election Campaign (page 9) ▶

L A B E L H E R E	Your first name and initial: Jack C.	Last name: Allen	Your social security number: 222 : 80 : 6002

If a joint return, spouse's first name and initial	Last name	Spouse's social security number : :

Home address (number and street). If you have a P.O. box, see page 9.   Apt. no.
100 Maple Street

City, town or post office, state, and ZIP code. If you have a foreign address, see page 9.
Anytown, MO 12345

▲ You **must** enter your SSN(s) above. ▲

Checking a box below will not change your tax or refund.

Check here if you, or your spouse if a joint return, want $3 to go to this fund . . . ▶ ✔ **You**   ☐ **Spouse**

Income

Attach Form(s) W-2 here.

Enclose, but do not attach, any payment.

1 Wages, salaries, and tips. This should be shown in box 1 of your Form(s) W-2. Attach your Form(s) W-2. | 1 |

2 Taxable interest. If the total is over $1,500, you cannot use Form 1040EZ. | 2 |

3 Unemployment compensation and Alaska Permanent Fund dividends (see page 11). | 3 |

4 Add lines 1, 2, and 3. This is your **adjusted gross income.** | 4 |

5 If someone can claim you (or your spouse if a joint return) as a dependent, check the applicable box(es) below and enter the amount from the worksheet on back.

☐ **You**   ☐ **Spouse**

If no one can claim you (or your spouse if a joint return), enter $8,950 if **single;** $17,900 if **married filing jointly.** See back for explanation. | 5 |

6 Subtract line 5 from line 4. If line 5 is larger than line 4, enter -0-. This is your **taxable income.** ▶ | 6 |

Payments and tax

7 Federal income tax withheld from box 2 of your Form(s) W-2. | 7 |

8a **Earned income credit (EIC)** (see page 12). | 8a |

b Nontaxable combat pay election.   8b | |

9 Recovery rebate credit (see worksheet on pages 17 and 18). | 9 |

10 Add lines 7, 8a, and 9. These are your **total payments.** ▶ | 10 |

11 **Tax.** Use the amount on **line 6 above** to find your tax in the tax table on pages 28–36 of the booklet. Then, enter the tax from the table on this line. | 11 |

Refund

Have it directly deposited! See page 18 and fill in 12b, 12c, and 12d or Form 8888.

12a If line 10 is larger than line 11, subtract line 11 from line 10. This is your **refund.** If Form 8888 is attached, check here ▶ ☐ | 12a |

▶ b Routing number | | ▶ c Type: ☐ Checking ☐ Savings

▶ d Account number | |

Amount you owe

13 If line 11 is larger than line 10, subtract line 10 from line 11. This is the **amount you owe.** For details on how to pay, see page 19. ▶ | 13 |

Third party designee

Do you want to allow another person to discuss this return with the IRS (see page 20)? ☐ **Yes.** Complete the following. ☐ **No**

Designee's name ▶ | Phone no. ▶ (   ) | Personal identification number (PIN) ▶ |

Sign here

Joint return? See page 6.

Keep a copy for your records.

Under penalties of perjury, I declare that I have examined this return, and to the best of my knowledge and belief, it is true, correct, and accurately lists all amounts and sources of income I received during the tax year. Declaration of preparer (other than the taxpayer) is based on all information of which the preparer has any knowledge.

Your signature	Date	Your occupation	Daytime phone number ( )
Spouse's signature. If a joint return, **both** must sign.	Date	Spouse's occupation	

Paid preparer's use only

Preparer's signature ▶		Date	Check if self-employed ☐	Preparer's SSN or PTIN
Firm's name (or yours if self-employed), address, and ZIP code			EIN	
			Phone no. ( )	

For Disclosure, Privacy Act, and Paperwork Reduction Act Notice, see page 37.   Cat. No. 11329W   Form **1040EZ** (2008)

EXERCISE
7.4

NAME: _____ CLASS PERIOD: _____

Is It Better to Get a Tax Refund or to Have Fewer Taxes Withheld? Part 2

Instructions: Use Jill's pay stub and Form W-2 to complete her 1040EZ; then answer the questions at the end of the exercise. You will need a copy of Illustration 7.1, Federal Tax Table for Form 1040EZ, to complete this exercise.

Jill's Pay Stub

Pay Check		Calculations Based on	
Weekly Gross Pay	$400.00	Tax Year	2008
Federal Withholding	$25.66	Gross Pay	$400.00
Social Security	$24.80	Pay Frequency	Weekly
Medicare	$5.80	Federal Filing Status	Single
Missouri Withholding	$9.00	# of Federal Allowances	1
Net Pay	$334.74	Additional Federal W/H	$0.00
		State	Missouri
		Filing Status	Single

Jill's W-2

22222	Void ☐	a Employee's social security number 608-40-1234	For Official Use Only ▶ OMB No. 1545-0008		
b Employer identification number (EIN) 12345678			1 Wages, tips, other compensation 20,800.00	2 Federal income tax withheld 1,334.50	
c Employer's name, address, and ZIP code Foo Foo Gourmet Coffee Shop 808 Oak Dr. Anytown, MO 12345			3 Social security wages 20,800.00	4 Social security tax withheld 1,289.60	
			5 Medicare wages and tips 20,800.00	6 Medicare tax withheld 301.60	
			7 Social security tips	8 Allocated tips	
d Control number			9 Advance EIC payment	10 Dependent care benefits	
e Employee's first name and initial Jill	Last name Jones	Suff. O.	11 Nonqualified plans	12a See instructions for box 12	
6 Sweetbriar Lane Anytown, MO 12345			13 Statutory employee ☐ Retirement plan ☐ Third-party sick pay ☐	12b	
			14 Other	12c	
				12d	
f Employee's address and ZIP code					

15 State	Employer's state ID number 7891011	16 State wages, tips, etc. 20,800.00	17 State income tax 475.00	18 Local wages, tips, etc.	19 Local income tax	20 Locality name

Form **W-2** Wage and Tax Statement   **2008**   Department of the Treasury—Internal Revenue Service
For Privacy Act and Paperwork Reduction

Jill's Form 1040EZ

Form **1040EZ**	Department of the Treasury—Internal Revenue Service **Income Tax Return for Single and Joint Filers With No Dependents** (99) **2008**		OMB No. 1545-0074

Label (See page 9.)

Use the IRS label.

Otherwise, please print or type.

Presidential Election Campaign (page 9) ▶

L A B E L H E R E	Your first name and initial **Jill O.**	Last name **Jones**	Your social security number **608 : 40 : 1234**
	If a joint return, spouse's first name and initial	Last name	Spouse's social security number ___ : ___ : ___
	Home address (number and street). If you have a P.O. box, see page 9. **6 Sweetbriar Lane**	Apt. no.	▲ You **must** enter your SSN(s) above. ▲
	City, town or post office, state, and ZIP code. If you have a foreign address, see page 9. **Anytown, MO 12345**		Checking a box below will not change your tax or refund.

Check here if you, or your spouse if a joint return, want $3 to go to this fund . . . ▶ ☐ **You**   ☐ **Spouse**

Income

Attach Form(s) W-2 here.

Enclose, but do not attach, any payment.

1	Wages, salaries, and tips. This should be shown in box 1 of your Form(s) W-2. Attach your Form(s) W-2.	1	
2	Taxable interest. If the total is over $1,500, you cannot use Form 1040EZ.	2	
3	Unemployment compensation and Alaska Permanent Fund dividends (see page 11).	3	
4	Add lines 1, 2, and 3. This is your **adjusted gross income.**	4	
5	If someone can claim you (or your spouse if a joint return) as a dependent, check the applicable box(es) below and enter the amount from the worksheet on back. ☐ **You** ☐ **Spouse** If no one can claim you (or your spouse if a joint return), enter $8,950 if **single;** $17,900 if **married filing jointly.** See back for explanation.	5	
6	Subtract line 5 from line 4. If line 5 is larger than line 4, enter -0-. This is your **taxable income.** ▶	6	

Payments and tax

7	Federal income tax withheld from box 2 of your Form(s) W-2.	7	
8a	**Earned income credit (EIC)** (see page 12).	8a	
b	Nontaxable combat pay election. 8b		
9	Recovery rebate credit (see worksheet on pages 17 and 18).	9	
10	Add lines 7, 8a, and 9. These are your **total payments.** ▶	10	
11	**Tax.** Use the amount on **line 6 above** to find your tax in the tax table on pages 28–36 of the booklet. Then, enter the tax from the table on this line.	11	

Refund

Have it directly deposited! See page 18 and fill in 12b, 12c, and 12d or Form 8888.

12a	If line 10 is larger than line 11, subtract line 11 from line 10. This is your **refund.** If Form 8888 is attached, check here ▶ ☐	12a	
▶ b	Routing number ⎢⎢⎢⎢⎢⎢⎢⎢⎢ ▶ c Type: ☐ Checking ☐ Savings		
▶ d	Account number ⎢⎢⎢⎢⎢⎢⎢⎢⎢		

Amount you owe

13	If line 11 is larger than line 10, subtract line 10 from line 11. This is the **amount you owe.** For details on how to pay, see page 19. ▶	13	

Third party designee

Do you want to allow another person to discuss this return with the IRS (see page 20)?   ☐ **Yes.** Complete the following.   ☐ **No**

Designee's name ▶	Phone no. ▶ ( )	Personal identification number (PIN) ▶ ⎢⎢⎢⎢⎢

Sign here

Joint return? See page 6.

Keep a copy for your records.

Under penalties of perjury, I declare that I have examined this return, and to the best of my knowledge and belief, it is true, correct, and accurately lists all amounts and sources of income I received during the tax year. Declaration of preparer (other than the taxpayer) is based on all information of which the preparer has any knowledge.

Your signature	Date	Your occupation	Daytime phone number ( )
Spouse's signature. If a joint return, **both** must sign.	Date	Spouse's occupation	

Paid preparer's use only

Preparer's signature ▶		Date	Check if self-employed ☐	Preparer's SSN or PTIN
Firm's name (or yours if self-employed), address, and ZIP code ▶			EIN	
			Phone no. ( )	

For Disclosure, Privacy Act, and Paperwork Reduction Act Notice, see page 37.   Cat. No. 11329W   Form **1040EZ** (2008)

Questions:

a. What is Jill's weekly gross pay? What is her weekly net pay?

b. Why is Jill's net pay different from Jack's when their gross pay is the same? (Refer to Jack's pay stub on page 41.)

c. Does Jill owe taxes or get a refund?

d. What would you recommend to Jill about adjusting her withholding allowances for next year?

ILLUSTRATION
7.1

THEME 2 | Lesson 7: Uncle Sam Takes a Bite

Federal Tax Table for Form 1040EZ

2008 Tax Table – *Continued*

If Form 1040EZ, line 6, is – At least	But less than	And you are – Single	Married filing jointly
9,000			
9,000	9,050	953	903
9,050	9,100	960	908
9,100	9,150	968	913
9,150	9,200	975	918
9,200	9,250	983	923
9,250	9,300	990	928
9,300	9,350	998	933
9,350	9,400	1,005	938
9,400	9,450	1,013	943
9,450	9,500	1,020	948
9,500	9,550	1,028	953
9,550	9,600	1,035	958
9,600	9,650	1,043	963
9,650	9,700	1,050	968
9,700	9,750	1,058	973
9,750	9,800	1,065	978
9,800	9,850	1,073	983
9,850	9,900	1,080	988
9,900	9,950	1,088	993
9,950	10,000	1,095	998
10,000			
10,000	10,050	1,103	1,003
10,050	10,100	1,110	1,008
10,100	10,150	1,118	1,013
10,150	10,200	1,125	1,018
10,200	10,250	1,133	1,023
10,250	10,300	1,140	1,028
10,300	10,350	1,148	1,033
10,350	10,400	1,155	1,038
10,400	10,450	1,163	1,043
10,450	10,500	1,170	1,048
10,500	10,550	1,178	1,053
10,550	10,600	1,185	1,058
10,600	10,650	1,193	1,063
10,650	10,700	1,200	1,068
10,700	10,750	1,208	1,073
10,750	10,800	1,215	1,078
10,800	10,850	1,223	1,083
10,850	10,900	1,230	1,088
10,900	10,950	1,238	1,093
10,950	11,000	1,245	1,098
11,000			
11,000	11,050	1,253	1,103
11,050	11,100	1,260	1,108
11,100	11,150	1,268	1,113
11,150	11,200	1,275	1,118
11,200	11,250	1,283	1,123
11,250	11,300	1,290	1,128
11,300	11,350	1,298	1,133
11,350	11,400	1,305	1,138
11,400	11,450	1,313	1,143
11,450	11,500	1,320	1,148
11,500	11,550	1,328	1,153
11,550	11,600	1,335	1,158
11,600	11,650	1,343	1,163
11,650	11,700	1,350	1,168
11,700	11,750	1,358	1,173
11,750	11,800	1,365	1,178
11,800	11,850	1,373	1,183
11,850	11,900	1,380	1,188
11,900	11,950	1,388	1,193
11,950	12,000	1,395	1,198

If Form 1040EZ, line 6, is – At least	But less than	And you are – Single	Married filing jointly
12,000			
12,000	12,050	1,403	1,203
12,050	12,100	1,410	1,208
12,100	12,150	1,418	1,213
12,150	12,200	1,425	1,218
12,200	12,250	1,433	1,223
12,250	12,300	1,440	1,228
12,300	12,350	1,448	1,233
12,350	12,400	1,455	1,238
12,400	12,450	1,463	1,243
12,450	12,500	1,470	1,248
12,500	12,550	1,478	1,253
12,550	12,600	1,485	1,258
12,600	12,650	1,493	1,263
12,650	12,700	1,500	1,268
12,700	12,750	1,508	1,273
12,750	12,800	1,515	1,278
12,800	12,850	1,523	1,283
12,850	12,900	1,530	1,288
12,900	12,950	1,538	1,293
12,950	13,000	1,545	1,298
13,000			
13,000	13,050	1,553	1,303
13,050	13,100	1,560	1,308
13,100	13,150	1,568	1,313
13,150	13,200	1,575	1,318
13,200	13,250	1,583	1,323
13,250	13,300	1,590	1,328
13,300	13,350	1,598	1,333
13,350	13,400	1,605	1,338
13,400	13,450	1,613	1,343
13,450	13,500	1,620	1,348
13,500	13,550	1,628	1,353
13,550	13,600	1,635	1,358
13,600	13,650	1,643	1,363
13,650	13,700	1,650	1,368
13,700	13,750	1,658	1,373
13,750	13,800	1,665	1,378
13,800	13,850	1,673	1,383
13,850	13,900	1,680	1,388
13,900	13,950	1,688	1,393
13,950	14,000	1,695	1,398
14,000			
14,000	14,050	1,703	1,403
14,050	14,100	1,710	1,408
14,100	14,150	1,718	1,413
14,150	14,200	1,725	1,418
14,200	14,250	1,733	1,423
14,250	14,300	1,740	1,428
14,300	14,350	1,748	1,433
14,350	14,400	1,755	1,438
14,400	14,450	1,763	1,443
14,450	14,500	1,770	1,448
14,500	14,550	1,778	1,453
14,550	14,600	1,785	1,458
14,600	14,650	1,793	1,463
14,650	14,700	1,800	1,468
14,700	14,750	1,808	1,473
14,750	14,800	1,815	1,478
14,800	14,850	1,823	1,483
14,850	14,900	1,830	1,488
14,900	14,950	1,838	1,493
14,950	15,000	1,845	1,498

If Form 1040EZ, line 6, is – At least	But less than	And you are – Single	Married filing jointly
15,000			
15,000	15,050	1,853	1,503
15,050	15,100	1,860	1,508
15,100	15,150	1,868	1,513
15,150	15,200	1,875	1,518
15,200	15,250	1,883	1,523
15,250	15,300	1,890	1,528
15,300	15,350	1,898	1,533
15,350	15,400	1,905	1,538
15,400	15,450	1,913	1,543
15,450	15,500	1,920	1,548
15,500	15,550	1,928	1,553
15,550	15,600	1,935	1,558
15,600	15,650	1,943	1,563
15,650	15,700	1,950	1,568
15,700	15,750	1,958	1,573
15,750	15,800	1,965	1,578
15,800	15,850	1,973	1,583
15,850	15,900	1,980	1,588
15,900	15,950	1,988	1,593
15,950	16,000	1,995	1,598
16,000			
16,000	16,050	2,003	1,603
16,050	16,100	2,010	1,609
16,100	16,150	2,018	1,616
16,150	16,200	2,025	1,624
16,200	16,250	2,033	1,631
16,250	16,300	2,040	1,639
16,300	16,350	2,048	1,646
16,350	16,400	2,055	1,654
16,400	16,450	2,063	1,661
16,450	16,500	2,070	1,669
16,500	16,550	2,078	1,676
16,550	16,600	2,085	1,684
16,600	16,650	2,093	1,691
16,650	16,700	2,100	1,699
16,700	16,750	2,108	1,706
16,750	16,800	2,115	1,714
16,800	16,850	2,123	1,721
16,850	16,900	2,130	1,729
16,900	16,950	2,138	1,736
16,950	17,000	2,145	1,744
17,000			
17,000	17,050	2,153	1,751
17,050	17,100	2,160	1,759
17,100	17,150	2,168	1,766
17,150	17,200	2,175	1,774
17,200	17,250	2,183	1,781
17,250	17,300	2,190	1,789
17,300	17,350	2,198	1,796
17,350	17,400	2,205	1,804
17,400	17,450	2,213	1,811
17,450	17,500	2,220	1,819
17,500	17,550	2,228	1,826
17,550	17,600	2,235	1,834
17,600	17,650	2,243	1,841
17,650	17,700	2,250	1,849
17,700	17,750	2,258	1,856
17,750	17,800	2,265	1,864
17,800	17,850	2,273	1,871
17,850	17,900	2,280	1,879
17,900	17,950	2,288	1,886
17,950	18,000	2,295	1,894

If Form 1040EZ, line 6, is – At least	But less than	And you are – Single	Married filing jointly
18,000			
18,000	18,050	2,303	1,901
18,050	18,100	2,310	1,909
18,100	18,150	2,318	1,916
18,150	18,200	2,325	1,924
18,200	18,250	2,333	1,931
18,250	18,300	2,340	1,939
18,300	18,350	2,348	1,946
18,350	18,400	2,355	1,954
18,400	18,450	2,363	1,961
18,450	18,500	2,370	1,969
18,500	18,550	2,378	1,976
18,550	18,600	2,385	1,984
18,600	18,650	2,393	1,991
18,650	18,700	2,400	1,999
18,700	18,750	2,408	2,006
18,750	18,800	2,415	2,014
18,800	18,850	2,423	2,021
18,850	18,900	2,430	2,029
18,900	18,950	2,438	2,036
18,950	19,000	2,445	2,044
19,000			
19,000	19,050	2,453	2,051
19,050	19,100	2,460	2,059
19,100	19,150	2,468	2,066
19,150	19,200	2,475	2,074
19,200	19,250	2,483	2,081
19,250	19,300	2,490	2,089
19,300	19,350	2,498	2,096
19,350	19,400	2,505	2,104
19,400	19,450	2,513	2,111
19,450	19,500	2,520	2,119
19,500	19,550	2,528	2,126
19,550	19,600	2,535	2,134
19,600	19,650	2,543	2,141
19,650	19,700	2,550	2,149
19,700	19,750	2,558	2,156
19,750	19,800	2,565	2,164
19,800	19,850	2,573	2,171
19,850	19,900	2,580	2,179
19,900	19,950	2,588	2,186
19,950	20,000	2,595	2,194
20,000			
20,000	20,050	2,603	2,201
20,050	20,100	2,610	2,209
20,100	20,150	2,618	2,216
20,150	20,200	2,625	2,224
20,200	20,250	2,633	2,231
20,250	20,300	2,640	2,239
20,300	20,350	2,648	2,246
20,350	20,400	2,655	2,254
20,400	20,450	2,663	2,261
20,450	20,500	2,670	2,269
20,500	20,550	2,678	2,276
20,550	20,600	2,685	2,284
20,600	20,650	2,693	2,291
20,650	20,700	2,700	2,299
20,700	20,750	2,708	2,306
20,750	20,800	2,715	2,314
20,800	20,850	2,723	2,321
20,850	20,900	2,730	2,329
20,900	20,950	2,738	2,336
20,950	21,000	2,745	2,344

Introduction

Money Management

Do you know people who handle money carelessly? Lots of seemingly smart people are clueless about where they stand financially. There is Beverly, a professional woman, who calls the bank every two or three months to find out what the balance is in her checking account. She has never reconciled her checking account, so she never knows what her balance is. What Beverly still hasn't learned is that people at her bank don't know what Bev's real balance is either, because they don't know what checks Beverly has written that have not yet been cleared by the bank. Only Beverly knows that. And then there is Ben. Ben actually believes that he can write checks as long as he has blank ones to be used. Ben has been heard to say, "Why would the bank give me blank checks if I'm not supposed to use them?"

You don't have to be like Ben and Bev. You can get on the fast track to wealth by becoming good at managing money. To manage your money well, you need to know some basic information, use some common sense, and then take action. We recommend three steps.

First, get a grip on your spending. How can you do that? In the old-fashioned way. Set up a budget. Make a list of your income and expenses. Then subtract your expenses from your income. If you have any surplus cash, plan how you will use it. Do this each month. Maybe you will learn that now is the time to get started investing in a mutual fund or stock account.

Second, get to know the various services offered by financial institutions in your community. Checking accounts are among the most common financial services people use, but there are many others including ATMs, online banking, direct deposits, savings accounts, credit cards, installment loans, student loans, retirement accounts, and certificates of deposit. Among the many types of financial institutions, four

important ones are commercial banks, savings and loans, credit unions and broker-age firms. Open an account now at one or more financial institutions. Start with checking and savings accounts, but don't wait long to start other, more rewarding savings programs. Becoming wealthy is within your grasp. Starting to save when you are young is a good idea.

Finally, learn how to protect yourself against risk. All choices involve risk, but some risks are greater than others. Buying insurance is a common way to reduce risk. There are many kinds of insurance to consider including auto, health, renter's, homeowner's, life, and disability. The type and amount of insurance you need will change as you get older and the value of your assets increases.

The best thing about these three tips and others covered in these lessons is that none of it is overly difficult. It might take some work, but you can learn this stuff. Your efforts now can have a big payoff later.

NAME: _____ CLASS PERIOD: _____

Budgets Are Beautiful Call-In Show

Radio Host Budget Bob

Hello, financial health fans! Welcome to the nation's newest financial advice show, Budgets Are Beautiful. This is the radio call-in show that lets you, the radio listener, get the latest advice on how to manage your family finances. Today our topic is how to improve your skills at managing your family's finances. Our guest today is a successful family financial planner, Dr. Penny Saver. Dr. Saver has helped hundreds of families and has a Ph.D., M.A., and an S.U.V. Hello, Dr. Saver. Welcome to the show.

Dr. Saver

Hello Bob, and hello to all those people who are tuned in today. I am ready to take your questions.

Budget Bob

Here is our first caller: Connie from Connecticut. You're on the air, Connie.

Connie

Hi, Dr. Saver. I am having a disagreement with my husband regarding the meaning of some financial vocabulary. He heard someone on another call-in show talking about how to spend disposable income. My husband laughed and said that all of our income is disposable. He said that we dispose of all our income by the end of every month. Sometimes we dispose of our income before the end of the month. I think he was joking, but could you tell me: What do financial planners mean by disposable income?

Dr. Saver

Actually, your husband was not too far off. Disposable income is the money that you have left to spend or save as you wish after you pay your taxes, Social Security, and the other deductions that have been taken out of your gross pay. It is sometimes called net income. While disposable income can be used in many ways, most families have important financial obligations. Rent, car payments, and food bills add up quickly, so tough choices need to be made.

Budget Bob

That sounds kind of gloomy, Dr. Saver. Do you have any advice for Connie and her husband on how to get better use out of their disposable income?

Dr. Saver

Financial planners suggest that setting up and sticking to a family budget is the first step toward financial success. I advise families to start by setting a monthly budget.

To do this, you make a list of your income and expenses. Under income, list all the money you anticipate earning for the year. For most people, most income will be what they earn from their jobs. If your income varies month to month, divide your annual income by 12 and use the answer for the monthly income in your budget.

Then list your expenses. To help make sure your list of expenses is complete, look at last year's bills, credit card statements, and bank records. To capture the amount you spend on items you buy with cash, keep track of your out-of-pocket spending for a month or two on a small tablet.   After you've done all this, you will have a good idea of where your money goes each month. Common expenses are rent, car payments, insurance, groceries, and so forth. Don't forget to list your savings amounts for each of your goals. If you wait to save what's left at the end of the month, you will never begin saving.

Now, subtract your expenses from your income. I hope that this is a positive number! If it is—if you have more income than expenses—then you have surplus cash that can be put to other uses. If, however, the number is negative, then you will need to cut your expenses, increase your income, or use some of your savings to get through the month.

Budget Bob

Here is our next caller: Calvin from California. You're on the air, Cal.

Calvin

Hello Dr. Saver. Thanks for taking my call. My wife and I started to write a monthly budget and we learned right away that not all expenses are the same. Some seem to stay pretty much the same each month while others change. Do other people have this same situation? Can you comment on the different types of household expenses?

Dr. Saver

Great question! Families ordinarily have what we call fixed expenses and variable expenses. Fixed expenses are ones that are relatively constant each month. These are a family's definite obligations such as a house payment, rent payment, car payment, and medical insurance. These expenses are hard to change in the short term, so we say they are "fixed." Variable expenses are ones that are likely to change in the short term. Examples include telephone bills, groceries, medical bills not covered by insurance, entertainment, recreation, charge account purchases, and so forth. These are expenses over which you have more short-term control. Occasional expenses or periodic expenses are those that occur once or a few times a year. Personal property taxes, income taxes, car insurance, birthday gifts and holiday gifts are examples of expenses that get some people in trouble because they forget to plan for them.

Budget Bob

Dr. Saver, I sometimes hear advisors say, "Pay yourself first." In other words, set money aside from your disposable income to put into your savings plan. How does this idea of "pay yourself first" fit into the family's expenses?

Dr. Saver

I tell my clients to include their savings goals in the fixed expenses part of their budget. I like this approach because it shows how important saving is to individual and family financial health. Under the saving part of the budget, a family or individual could list funds saved for emergencies, as well as other cash set aside for long-term savings and investments.

Budget Bob

Here is our next caller, Minnie from Minnesota. You're on the air, Minnie.

Minnie

I just love this show, Dr. Saver. Here is my question. My sister Emily told me that she heard on television that people might have high incomes and still have a low net girth. What's all this about net girth? Is it true that people who have high incomes are also thin?

Dr. Saver

Minnie, I think that you misunderstood your sister. I think she was referring to the idea of net worth, not net girth. Let me explain. People can have high incomes and still not be wealthy. When we measure wealth, we are measuring net worth. Here is how to figure your net worth. Net worth is determined by two factors. First, list your assets and their value. Assets are what a person owns, including the value of any savings, house, car, and personal possessions. Next, list your liabilities. Liabilities are the money you owe others such as payments on a home mortgage, car loan, credit card debt, college loans, and so forth. If your assets are greater than your liabilities, then you have a positive net worth. If your liabilities are greater than your assets, then you have a negative net worth. Individuals can have a large income and, because of their liabilities, still have a negative net worth.

Minnie

Can I follow up on that last point? Do you mean to say that you can't tell whether a person is wealthy just by knowing where they live, what they drive, and where they travel?

Dr. Saver

That is exactly what I mean, Minnie. People who live in big homes, drive extravagant cars, and take around-the-world cruises probably have high incomes. That does not mean that they are wealthy. We measure wealth by calculating net worth. Many people of modest income have achieved a high net worth—many are millionaires—by living below their means.

Budget Bob

Well, Dr. Saver, that is all the time we have for today's show. Thank you for being with us.

Dr. Saver

You're welcome, Bob. Thanks for inviting me.

Budget Bob

Be sure to join us tomorrow when we will speak to Ms. Bonnie Bonds, another financial advisor. Bonnie's topic is "What Is Gross about Your Gross Income?" We hope you will tune in to the show tomorrow. We will be waiting for your call.

Questions:

a. What is disposable income?

b. What does Dr. Saver recommend as the three parts of a family budget?

c. What are fixed and variable expenses? Use examples to illustrate each.

d. What does "pay yourself first" mean?

e. What is net worth?

NAME: _____ CLASS PERIOD: _____

John and Marcia: Monthly Spending Plan 1

John and Marcia are a young married couple. They have a two-year-old child named Ashley and a goldfish named Shark. John manages a local shoe store. Marcia recently graduated from college and is a manager-trainee at a local bank. Their combined monthly income is $5,200. They want to have a successful marriage, and they want to be financially successful.

John and Marcia have enough income to provide an adequate lifestyle. Their apartment is comfortable but not lavish. They take care of themselves, Ashley, and Shark with sensible diets, exercise, and medical care. They view maintaining health, life, disability, and renter's insurance as essential. They pay for child care at Terrific Tots Day Care so that both of them can work. They keep up with all their financial commitments, such as making payments on Marcia's college loan. They regard saving for retirement as important. Like other individuals, they are locked into their fixed expenses, but they have more flexibility with the variable expenses.

Marcia and John know that they want a second car. It is difficult to manage their complex schedules—work, day care, grocery shopping, and trips to the doctor—with only one car. They recently set a goal to save up enough money in one year for the down payment on a second car.

John and Marcia are regular savers. They practice the idea of "paying yourself first." They currently have $175 withheld each month from their paychecks to provide a fund for emergencies. They plan to have $400 taken from their paychecks each month for the next year to enable them to make a $2,700 down payment on the second car.

Listed below are the "before" and "after" fixed expenses. The only item that has changed in the **After** column is "Savings withheld." Go to the listing of John and Marcia's variable expenses. Figure out where John and Marcia can draw the additional money for savings from their variable expenses. Also, answer the questions at the end of this exercise.

Monthly Budget	Before	After
Total Income (both spouses work)	$5,200	$5,200
Fixed Expenses		
Housing	750	750
Life and disability insurance	325	325
Renter's insurance	15	15
Automobile insurance	80	80
Student loan	100	100
Savings withheld	175	400
Federal and State taxes	630	630
Social Security	400	400
Pension fund withheld	80	80
Total Fixed Expenses	$2,555	$2,780

Variable Expenses	Before	After
Meals (at home)	300	
Meals (away from home)	250	
Utilities	315	
Automobile fuel, maintenance	290	
Medical care	230	
Child care	205	
Clothing	195	
Gifts and contributions	60	
Magazines and newspapers	10	
Home furnishings and appliances	200	
Personal Care	50	
Entertainment	260	
Vacation	120	
Credit Card	100	
Miscellaneous/personal	60	
Total variable expenses	**$2,645**	
Total expenses	**$5,200**	**$5,200**

Questions:

a. What are some examples of John and Marcia's fixed expenses?

b. What are some examples of John and Marcia's variable expenses?

c. John and Marcia have decided to practice the "pay yourself first" approach to saving for a second car. How do they pay themselves first?

d. Examine John and Marcia's monthly spending plan above. What sacrifices do you think John and Marcia should make in their variable expenses to meet their goal? Note: At-home food expenses can't be reduced below $220.

e. What are the benefits and costs of your recommended decisions for John and Marcia?

NAME: _____ CLASS PERIOD: _____

John and Marcia: Monthly Spending Plan 2

One year later, John and Marcia are pleased with their financial decisions. They have been able to reduce their expenses to purchase the second car. They have enjoyed the convenience of owning a second car, their income has increased, and Marcia's college loan has been paid off. But new challenges have arrived. The car payment is greater than the college loan was. While having two cars has made life much better, the extra car has added to insurance and car expenses. Also, increased income means the couple pays more in taxes and Social Security.

Marcia and John know that to be financially successful they need to begin acquiring better assets. Owning a home is on the top of their personal and financial wish list. They have set a goal to save $15,600 in four years for a down payment, closing costs, and other expenses related to the purchase of their home. They had been saving $400 per month in order to afford a down payment on a second car. They now plan to have another $100 taken out of their paychecks for the next year to start their down-payment fund for a home. Note that $175 of this monthly saving is set aside for emergencies.

Listed below are the **Before** and **After** fixed expenses for John and Marcia's new savings plan. The third column represents their anticipated expenses as homeowners. The only fixed expense that will change is "Savings withheld." Figure out where they can draw the additional money for savings from their variable expenses. Enter your new amounts in the chart on the next page. Also, answer the questions at the end of the exercise.

Monthly Budget	Before	After	Homeowners
Total Income (both spouses work)	**$5,400**	**$5,400**	**$5,400**
Fixed Expenses			
Housing (rent or own)	750	750	840
Life and disability insurance	325	325	325
Homeowners insurance and taxes	15	15	210
Automobile insurance	130	130	130
Car loan	400	400	400
Savings withheld	400	500	400
Federal and State taxes	670	670	420
Social Security	415	415	415
Pension fund withheld	100	100	100
Total Fixed Expenses	**$3,205**	**$3,305**	**$3,240**

Variable Expenses	Before	After	Homeowners
Meals (at home)	315		
Meals (away from home)	150		
Utilities	300		
Automobile fuel, maintenance	400		
Medical care	230		
Child care	175		
Clothing	75		
Gifts and contributions	50		
Magazines and newspapers	15		
Home furnishings and appliances	40		
Personal Care	70		
Entertainment	180		
Vacation	100		
Credit Card	30		
Miscellaneous/personal	65		
Total variable expenses	**$2,195**	**$2,095**	**$2,160**
Total expenses	**$5,400**	**$5,400**	**$5,400**

Questions:

a. What is John and Marcia's new financial goal?

b. Examine the monthly spending plan above. What sacrifices do you think John and Marcia should make in their variable expenses to meet their goal? Enter new amounts for spending in the **After** column of Variable expenses. Note: At-home meal expenses cannot be reduced below $220.

c. What are the benefits and costs of your recommended decisions for John and Marcia?

NAME: _____ CLASS PERIOD: _____

Can John and Marcia Afford the Home of Their Dreams?

John and Marcia are saving money for a $10,000 down payment on a $150,000 home. In addition they are saving money to cover other costs (such as closing costs) that will be incurred when they purchase their new home. Use the new information below to determine whether John and Marcia can afford the home of their dreams.

New Information:

Use the table on the next page to determine the monthly house payment for a 30-year, fixed-rate mortgage loan at 6 percent. What would the monthly payment be for this loan? _____ (Hint: $150,000 – down payment = loan amount.)

To use the table, go down the column on the left to find the loan amount you want and follow across to the interest rate available. The figure on the table represents your mortgage payment of principal and interest (PI). For example, a $100,000 mortgage with an interest rate of 6.5 percent would have a monthly payment of $632.

The monthly payment covers Principal and Interest (PI), but John and Marcia also would need to pay for insurance and real estate taxes (TI), which total $210 each month. So their total house payment, which includes PITI, equals _____.

As homeowners John and Marcia will have to pay higher utility costs. They expect to budget $365 per month for utility payments.

One of the benefits of homeowner-ship is the ability to reduce your in-come taxes by deducting mortgage interest expenses. If they become homeowners, John and Marcia will pay $3,000 less annually in state and federal income taxes during the first year (which means their fixed expenses in this category would decline by a monthly amount of $250).

Loan Amount	Interest 6%	Interest 6.5%	Interest 7%	Interest 7.5%
$100,000	$600	$632	$665	$699
$110,000	$660	$695	$732	$769
$120,000	$720	$758	$798	$839
$130,000	$780	$822	$865	$909
$140,000	$840	$895	$932	$979
$150,000	$900	$948	$1,049	$1,101
$160,000	$960	$1,011	$1,065	$1,119
$170,000	$1,020	$1,074	$1,131	$1,189
$180,000	$1,080	$1,138	$1,198	$1,259
$190,000	$1,140	$1,201	$1,264	$1,328
$200,000	$1,200	$1,264	$1,331	$1,398

Questions:

Do John and Marcia have enough flexibility in their budget to accommodate the additional costs of homeownership (mortgage payment, taxes, insurance, and higher utilities)?

If not, what are some expenses they may need to reduce in order to afford the home they want?   Enter their new variable expenses related to owning a home in the Homeowner column in the budget form from Exercise 8.2B.

A rule of thumb for some lenders is to qualify you for a mortgage if the payments you would incur meet two criteria: a) the mortgage payment with taxes and insurance will be less than 28 percent of your monthly gross income, and b) the monthly mortgage payment of principal, interest, taxes, and insurance plus other monthly consumer debt (such as a car loan and credit card payments) will not exceed 36 percent of your gross monthly income. Would the loan John and Marcia are considering meet these lending criteria?

$5,400 x .28 _____

$5,400 x .36 _____

Do you think John and Marcia can afford to pay 28 percent of their monthly gross income as a monthly house payment?   Why or why not?

NAME: _____ CLASS PERIOD: _____

What Are Financial Institutions?

Four Common Financial Institutions

Financial institutions help people manage their money, protect it, and make it grow. People often use different types of financial institutions at different stages of their lives. Of these institutions, we will examine four:

- Commercial banks
- Savings and loan associations (S&Ls)
- Credit unions
- Brokerage firms

In the past, each type of financial institution offered specific and limited services. Banks took deposits to be placed in checking accounts, savings accounts, and certificates of deposit, and they granted credit (often in the form of loans) to qualified individuals. Savings and loans offered savings accounts and home mortgages. Credit unions, a type of member-owned cooperative, made low-interest loans available to their members. Brokerage firms bought and sold stocks for customers on an exchange, and offered other financial services.

Deregulation in the financial industry has blurred the lines between these institutions and increased competition among them. Deregulation means that laws have been enacted to remove some of the restrictions (or regulations) that previously affected the industries in question. For example, savings and loans now can offer checking accounts and many types of loans in addition to home mortgages. Many commercial banks now can offer brokerage services.

Overview of Financial Services

1. Deposit Services

Types	Characteristics
Checking accounts	Convenience and safety for account holders. People can pay by check or debit card instead of cash. They retain a record of their transactions.
Savings accounts and certificates of deposits (CDs)	Safe places to let money grow; interest is earned on deposits.
Automated teller machines (ATMs)	Easy access to money from multiple locations, 24 hours a day.
Direct deposits and automatic withdrawals	Enable account holders to deposit money or pay bills automatically.
Online banking	Information about deposits, payments, statements, and all transactions is immediately available online, with only a few key strokes, 24 hours a day. Users can make payments without writing checks.
Deposit insurance	Guarantees that deposits are insured by the federal government for up to $250,000 per depositor. Agencies providing this insurance are the FDIC (for banks and S&Ls) or the NCUA (for credit unions).

2. Credit Services

Types	Characteristics
Credit cards	Enable card holders to access credit (for purchases) conveniently up to the amount of an approved credit limit.
Installment loans and credit lines	Provide opportunities to borrow money for major items such as a new or used automobile, education, home improvement, and other personal or household items.
Mortgages	Provide opportunities to borrow for the purchase of a home.
Home equity loans	Enable home owners to borrow money against the equity in their homes.
Student loans	Provide opportunities to borrow money to pay for a college education (often at below-market rates).
Small business loans	Provide opportunities to borrow money for the financial needs of a small business.

3. Investment Services

Types	Characteristics
Retirement accounts (IRAs, SEPs, KEOGHs)	Enable people to save money toward retirement on a tax-deferred basis.
Stocks, bonds, and mutual funds	Enable people to invest in corporations and governments in order to meet their financial needs for the future.

Questions:

a. Name four common financial institutions.

b. How are financial institutions changing?

c. What are some common deposit services?

d. What are some common credit services?

e. What are some common investment services?

NAME: _____ CLASS PERIOD: _____

Checking Out Checking Accounts

Financial institutions offer many different services. Among the most widely used financial services is the checking account. A checking account allows you to deposit money into an account. You then can write checks, or use an ATM or debit card, to withdraw money from the account as you wish. A checking account also makes it easy to use online banking services to make payments. Checking accounts are sometimes called demand deposit accounts because depositors can demand or use the money in their accounts when they wish to do so. Only the depositors can write checks on the account. Financial institutions usually offer free or low-cost accounts which don't pay interest on account balances. Usually there is a required minimum balance on accounts that pay interest.

The checklist that follows provides an overview of steps involved in opening your first checking account.

Choosing a checking account	There are three main types of checking accounts: • Special account: Service fees are charged at a low, flat rate, with an additional fee for each check written. This account is often appropriate for a high school student. • Standard account: Low or no monthly fee with no check charge. Customers may sometimes avoid a fee by maintaining a minimum balance. • Interest-bearing account: Interest is paid if you maintain a minimum daily balance in your account during the month.
Opening a checking account	• Take identification to the bank officer who handles new checking accounts. • Choose the type of checking account that best fits your needs. • Complete a signature card. • Make an opening deposit
Making a deposit	• Know the parts of a deposit slip. See the model in **Illustration 9.1**. • Write the date. • Write the amount of currency and coins to be deposited in the box marked "cash." • If checks are being deposited, write in the amount of each check. • Total the cash and check amounts. • Subtract any cash you wish to receive back. You may have to sign the deposit slip if you are receiving cash. • Keep a copy of the deposit receipt for your records. • Record the date and the amount of the deposit in your check register. Add the amount of the deposit to the balance.

ATMs and debit cards	• Automated teller machines (ATMs) allow you to conveniently deposit, withdraw, or transfer funds from your account, and to verify your account balance.
	• **Illustration 9.2** shows withdrawal and deposit receipts from ATMs.
	• ATMs require you to use a PIN (personal identification number) when you make a transaction.
	• Deposits made using ATMs may not be immediately available.
	• Availability of funds deposited at an ATM depends on the time of day the deposit is made and whether or not the ATM is owned by your financial institution. Depending on these factors, it may take several days before the deposited funds are available for use.
	• A debit card is issued by many financial institutions.
	• A debit card allows you to have the amount of a purchase withdrawn directly and immediately from your checking account and transferred to another party.
	• Be sure to keep receipts when you use your debit card; record the transactions in your check register, including any additional charges.
Phone banking	• Phone banking is a service provided by financial institutions which allows customers to perform transactions over the phone.
	• Most phone banks use passwords to ensure secure transactions with either an automated phone system or a live banking associate.
	• Bill paying, transferring funds between accounts, account information, etc., can all be performed over the phone.
Online banking	• Online banking connects you to your account over the Internet, with secure connections 24/7.
	• Online banking allows you to pay bills, transfer funds between accounts, or just check your balance at any time.
	• To pay bills online, you only have to enter the bill information and the account you want to use to pay it.
	• If the bill has a fixed payment, you can schedule a recurring payment on a certain date; if the amount changes, you can enter a new payment each month.
	• Online banking sometimes requires that you know both your account number and your financial institution's routing number to complete transactions. See **Illustration 9.3** to identify these numbers on a check. A financial institution associate can help you identify these numbers, too.
	• Online banking also requires a username and password for security purposes. Keep this information private, just like your PIN.
	• Online banking keeps your balance in your bank accounts. All bank transactions are included in your online account. Your checks, debit transactions, and other activity will all appear on your statement.
	• Online accounts offer both paper statements and online statements.
	• Online banking is available through banks in your community and through "virtual banks."

Endorsing a check	• An endorsement is a signature on the back of a check instructing the bank as to how the check may be cashed.
	• A blank endorsement is simply your signature on the back of the check. This makes the check as good as cash to anybody who holds it.
	• A restrictive endorsement tags a check for a specific purpose, such as for deposit only to a checking or savings account.
	• A special endorsement allows you to transfer the check to another person. No one except the person named in the endorsement may cash or deposit the check. Not all banks will honor this type of endorsement.
	• It is usually a good idea to wait until you are at the bank before endorsing your check, since an endorsed check can be cashed by the person who is holding it.
Writing a check	• Know the parts of a check. See the completed check in **Illustration 9.4.**
	• Complete all the parts of the check including date, "pay to the order of" (payee), numeric amount, written amount, and signature line. If you wish, complete the memo line to indicate the purpose of the check.
	• Use a pen.
	• Write clearly.
	• Sign your name as it appears on your signature card.
	• When you make a mistake, write "Void" on the check and keep the voided check for your records.
	• Be sure that you have enough money in your account to cover each check you write.
	• Record the number, date, payee, and amount of the check in your check register. Subtract the amount of the check from the balance.
	• Make sure to maintain a record of all automatic payments and on-line banking transactions you make using your checking account.
Reconciling your checkbook	• Financial institutions send a monthly statement that summarizes the activity of your checking account including deposits, checks written, service charges, and any interest earned.
	• Compare your checkbook register to the monthly statement. Check off deposits and withdrawals. Record in the register any service charges or interest earned listed on the bank statement but not in the register.
	• Use the printed form sent by the financial institution with your statement to reconcile your checking account.
	• Write the ending balance as shown on the statement.
	• Add deposits to the ending balance that are listed in the register but not on the statement.
	• Subtract withdrawals listed in the register but not on the statement.
	• Note the adjusted balance; it should equal the checkbook register.
	• If the account does not balance, research possible explanations such as having missed checks that did not clear the account, fees charged, interest paid, calculation errors, or transposed numbers.

Questions:

a. What is a checking account?

b. Why is the signature card important when you open a checking account?

c. What kind of a checking account is appropriate for most high school students?

d. What is a blank endorsement for a check?

e. When should you void a check?

f. What is a debit card?

g. What are some features of online banking?

NAME: _____ CLASS PERIOD: _____

Keeping a Checking Account

Suppose that you have a checking account. Imagine that you are using your debit/ATM card, writing checks to the businesses listed below, and depositing money in the checking account. Complete the checks and the deposit slips correctly and keep a record of each transaction in the check register.

March 1   Opened account with $250 cash deposit

March 7   Debit card: $30 to CD Sales to buy some CDs

March 8   Debit card: $50 for sweater purchased at A. J. Vitullo Company

March 10   Check #0994: Paid $45.10 to the Acme Bicycle Shop for repairs to bicycle

March 12   Check #0995: Paid $10.00 to Happy Pets Store for pet supplies

March 14   Deposited $50 gift money into account

March 16   Check #0996: Paid $16 to Lawson High School for two tickets to basketball game

March 18   ATM withdrawal: Took $50 out of account for spending money

---

DEPOSIT TICKET

John Q. Public
123 Money Lane
Richmondville, NC 27710

DATE _____

_____

MyBank USA
123-457-7891
19204 W. Blank Check St.
New York City, New York

⑈0210000021⑈   374

CASH		
TOTAL FROM OTHER SIDE		
TOTAL		
LESS CASH RECEIVED		
TOTAL ITEMS	NET DEPOSIT	

BE SURE EACH ITEM IS PROPERLY ENDORSED

This deposit is accepted subject to verification, the provisions of the uniform commercial code and the rules and regulations of this financial organization. Deposits may not be available for immediate withdrawal.

DEPOSIT TICKET

John Q. Public
123 Money Lane
Richmondville, NC 27710

DATE _____

_____

MyBank USA
123-457-7891
19204 W. Blank Check St.
New York City, New York

⑆021000021⑆ 374

CASH		
TOTAL FROM OTHER SIDE		
TOTAL		
LESS CASH RECEIVED		
TOTAL ITEMS	NET DEPOSIT	

BE SURE EACH ITEM IS PROPERLY ENDORSED

This deposit is accepted subject to verification, the provisions of the uniform commercial code and the rules and regulations of this financial organization. Deposits may not be available for immediate withdrawal.

PLEASE BE SURE TO DEDUCT CHARGES THAT AFFECT YOUR ACCOUNT							
CHECK #	DATE	TRANSACTION DESCRIPTION	WITHDRAWAL/ TRANSACTIONS	√ T	FEE IF ANY	DEPOSIT/ ADDITIONS	BALANCE

John Q. Public
123 Money Lane
Richmondville, NC 27710

90-29304/2934
1930000000

CHECK No. 0994

DATE ____________

PAY TO THE ORDER OF ______________________ $ [ ]

______________________ DOLLARS

MyBank USA
123-457-7891
19204 W. Blank Check St.
New York City, New York

MEMO / NOTES: ____________ SIGNATURE: ____________

⑆053000196⑆ 000687941443⑈ 0994

John Q. Public
123 Money Lane
Richmondville, NC 27710

90-29304/2934
1930000000

CHECK No. 0995

DATE ____________

PAY TO THE ORDER OF ______________________ $ [ ]

______________________ DOLLARS

MyBank USA
123-457-7891
19204 W. Blank Check St.
New York City, New York

MEMO / NOTES: ____________ SIGNATURE: ____________

⑆053000196⑆ 000687941443⑈ 0995

John Q. Public
123 Money Lane
Richmondville, NC 27710

90-29304/2934
1930000000

CHECK No. 0996

DATE ____________

PAY TO THE ORDER OF ______________________ $ [ ]

______________________ DOLLARS

MyBank USA
123-457-7891
19204 W. Blank Check St.
New York City, New York

MEMO / NOTES: ____________ SIGNATURE: ____________

⑆053000196⑆ 000687941443⑈ 0996

NAME: _____ CLASS PERIOD: _____

Financial Services Survey

Basic Facts

Name of financial institution: _____

Address: _____

Total number of locations: _____ Hours/days: _____

Membership or other qualifications required to do business: _____

Type of institution (check one)
- ☐ Bank
- ☐ Brokerage firm
- ☐ Credit union
- ☐ Savings & loan association

Survey conducted (check one)
- ☐ By phone
- ☐ In person
- ☐ Other _____

Check all financial services that this institution offers:
- ☐ Deposit services
- ☐ Checking accounts
- ☐ Savings accounts
- ☐ Certificates of deposit (CDs)
- ☐ Direct deposit and automatic withdrawal
- ☐ Deposit insurance (such as FDIC)
- ☐ Automated teller machines (ATMs)

Credit services
- ☐ Credit cards
- ☐ Installment loans
- ☐ Lines of credit
- ☐ Mortgages
- ☐ Home equity loans
- ☐ Student loans
- ☐ Small business loans

Investment services
- ☐ Retirement accounts (IRAs, SEPs, KEOGHs)
- ☐ Stocks and bonds
- ☐ Mutual funds

ILLUSTRATION

9.1

THEME 3 | Lesson 9: Banking Basics

NAME: _____ CLASS PERIOD: _____

A Completed Deposit Slip

Look at the sample deposit slip as you read the procedures for filling one out.

1. Write the current date.

2. Write the amount of currency and coin to be deposited in the area for "cash."

3. If checks are being deposited, write the amount of each check separately in the area for checks. Note: If you are depositing several checks, you will need to use the back of the deposit slip to enter the appropriate information.

4. Total the cash and checks and write that amount in the "total" box.

5. If you wish to receive cash back (usually when you are depositing only checks), write the amount in the "less cash received" box.

6. Correctly enter the "net deposit" by subtracting cash received from the "total" box.

7. If you are receiving cash, you will probably have to enter your signature on the deposit slip.

<table>
<tr><td rowspan="7" style="writing-mode: vertical-rl;">DEPOSIT TICKET</td><td colspan="2">Sarah Jones
123 Luxury Lane
Richmondville, NC 27710</td><td colspan="2">CASH</td><td>50</td><td>00</td></tr>
<tr><td></td><td></td><td></td><td></td><td>105</td><td>00</td></tr>
<tr><td></td><td></td><td></td><td></td><td>3</td><td>00</td></tr>
<tr><td></td><td></td><td></td><td></td><td>53</td><td>00</td></tr>
<tr><td>DATE JUNE 09, 2010</td><td></td><td colspan="2">TOTAL FROM OTHER SIDE</td><td></td><td></td></tr>
<tr><td></td><td></td><td colspan="2">TOTAL</td><td>211</td><td>00</td></tr>
<tr><td></td><td></td><td colspan="2">LESS CASH RECEIVED</td><td>50</td><td>00</td></tr>
</table>

MyBank USA
123-457-7891
19204 W. Blank Check St.
New York City, New York

TOTAL ITEMS   NET DEPOSIT   161 00
BE SURE EACH ITEM IS PROPERLY ENDORSED

This deposit is accepted subject to verification, the provisions of the uniform commercial code and the rules and regulations of this financial organization. Deposits may not be available for immediate withdrawal.

⑈0210000211⑆ 374

ILLUSTRATION
9.2

NAME: _____ CLASS PERIOD: _____

Using an ATM to Make a Deposit or Withdrawal

When you use an ATM to make a deposit, you may or may not need a deposit slip. Check with your bank. You may need only to key in the information for each check you deposit.

For withdrawals, you will receive a statement like this one, specifying the location of the transaction, the date and time, the amount of the withdrawal, any fee for the transaction, and the account balance after the transaction.

ATM Withdrawal Receipts

```
LOCATION: 13800 Biola University
          La Mirada


Card No: XXXXXXXXXXXX0717


    DATE        TIME      TERMINAL
  12/19/10    01:07PM     C01205


SEQ NBR:  6340 AMT          $20.00
          ATM OWNER FEE:     $2.00
          TOTAL             $22.00
          Balance:         $111.87
CHECKING WITHDRAWAL
```

ILLUSTRATION
9.3

THEME 3 | Lesson 9: Banking Basics

NAME: _____ CLASS PERIOD: _____

Know the Numbers

When you pay bills using your checking account, you can do so by writing a check or transferring the funds electronically. In order for funds to be transferred from your account, you will need to provide information about your financial institution and account.

The 9-digit routing number at the bottom-left of your check indentifies the financial institution where you have your account. The next group of numbers to the right is your account number. The last few digits are the check number. If you plan to pay bills online, bank by phone or by using the Internet, you may need to know both your account number and the routing number for your financial institution.

B Blank Check Foundation

90-29304/2934
1930000000

CHECK No. **1001**

DATE _____

PAY TO THE ORDER OF _____ $ [_____]

_____ DOLLARS

MyBank USA
123-457-7891
19204 W. Blank Check St.
New York City, New York

ACH R/T 123456789 ◄

MEMO / NOTES: _____   SIGNATURE: _____

⑆123456789⑆   000123456789⑈   1001

| ⑆123456789⑆ | 000123456789⑈ | 1001 | ACH/Routing |
| **ABA Check Routing Number** | **Account Number** | **Check Number** | **Transit Number** |

ILLUSTRATION
9.4

NAME: _____ CLASS PERIOD: _____

The Finer Points of Writing a Check

Look at the sample check as you read the procedures for filling one out.

1. Write the current date.

2. Write the name of the person or company you would like to pay. This person is called the payee. Start the name as close to the beginning of the line as possible. Draw a line to the end of the line so that no information can be added.

3. Enter the amount of the check in numbers, including a decimal point and cents. Start the numbers as close to the dollar sign as possible.

4. Enter the amount of the check in words. Start writing from the far left side of the line by entering the dollar amount in words, followed by the word "and"—e.g., "One Hundred and"; then write the cents amount as a fraction—e.g., 35/100. (If there are no cents, use 00/100.) Draw a line from the end of your writing to the end of the line so there is no additional room to insert words or numbers.

5. Sign your check the same way you signed the signature card when you opened your account.

6. You may wish to note the purpose of the check in the "memo" or "for" space to the left of the signature. You may also use this space to write the account or invoice number of the bill you are paying.

Sarah Jones
123 Luxury Lane
Richmondville, NC 27710

90-29304/2934
1930000000

CHECK No. __0 9 9 3__

DATE _April 28, 2010_

PAY TO THE ORDER OF __Sylvia Rodriguez__ $ | _100.35_ |

__One Hundred and 35/100__————————————— DOLLARS

MyBank USA
123-457-7891
19204 W. Blank Check St.
New York City, New York

MEMO / NOTES: __Used Furniture__   SIGNATURE: __Sarah Jones__

⑊053000196⑊   000687941443⑊   0993

ILLUSTRATION
9.5

THEME 3 | Lesson 9: Banking Basics

Online Banking Statement

Not so good at math? Let your online account help you. Online banking will show your resulting balance after each deposit, each check written, each debit card transaction. However, the balance shown is not always up to date. It is a good idea to keep a paper record of your transactions. Your account won't reflect deposits, debit card use, or checks until they are posted to your account. You can use the online statement to help you correct math errors as your reconcile any differences between your records and your monthly statement.

Balance: **$607.53**
Available Balance: **$587.53**

Pending Transactions

Date	Description	Debit	Credit
5/13/2010	ATM DEPOSIT KANSAS CITY, KS		$20.00

Posted Transactions

Type:	From:	To:	Chk Num:	
-ALL-	5/5/2010	5/14/2010		Display

Date	No.	Description	Debit	Credit	Balance
5/5/2010		CHECK CARD PURCHASE KANSAS CITY, MO	$6.98		$36.31
5/6/2010		DEPOSIT		$485.80	$522.11
5/7/2010		CHECK CARD PURCHASE ROELAND PARK, KS	$20.40		$501.71
5/9/2010		DEPOSIT		$200.00	$701.71
5/9/2010		PET STORE	$38.95		$662.76
5/10/2010		GROCERIES	$67.03		$595.73
5/12/2010		CHECK CARD PURCHASE KANSAS CITY, MO	$3.58		$592.15
5/13/2010		CHECK CARD PURCHASE KANSAS CITY, MO	$4.62		$587.53

NAME: _____ CLASS PERIOD: _____

Choices and Risks

All choices involve risk—some more than others, of course. Let's consider driving a car. Everyone knows that when you drive a car you risk having an accident. You could cause an accident yourself or another driver could cause an accident that involves you. How can you reduce the risk associated with having an automobile accident? You have three choices.

First, you could choose to stop driving—ride the bus, ride a bike, or walk. But the no-driving alternative may seem extreme. Let's examine the other choices. Second, you could become a safer driver. You could take a course in defensive driving; study the state's road-safety manual; pay attention in driver's education class; avoid driving during rush hours, on dangerous roads, and late at night. And, third, you could purchase auto insurance. You could purchase insurance to protect you from financial loss for money spent on car repairs, medical care, or lawsuits that result from an accident. With insurance, you might still have a wreck, but the consequences would not be as bad as they would have been if you did not have insurance.

Your choices about driving are similar to many other situations involving choice. Usually your best way to reduce risk is to take certain actions yourself. For example, to reduce health problems, you could resolve to eat right, get plenty of exercise, get enough sleep, avoid drugs, and so forth. Buying health insurance provides another way to reduce the risk of financial loss from health-care costs. To reduce the chances of loss from theft, you could install good locks on your doors, stop mail and newspaper deliveries when you are away, and keep areas around your house or apartment well lit. Buying home-

owner's or renter's insurance provides another way to reduce the risk of financial loss from theft.

The purpose of insurance is to spread risks out over many people. Let's consider an example. Imagine that the student council in a high school of 1,000 students wants to offer all students insurance against the theft of personal possessions from school lockers. The student council has decided to establish a locker insurance company. Suppose that students in this school have an average of $50 worth of personal stuff in each locker. Suppose further that, on average, 10 in every 1,000 lockers are broken into each year. In a typical year, students in the school lose a total of $500 ($50 of stuff x 10 locker break-ins) to locker theft. If all 1,000 students wish to buy insurance, it would cost:

$$\frac{\$500 \text{ loss}}{1000 \text{ students}} = \$.50 \text{ charge for each student for locker insurance}$$

If every student bought $.50 worth of locker insurance, all of them would be covered against losses they might incur from locker break-ins. This is fundamentally how insurance companies work. Insurance companies charge a fee (a premium) paid by customers to provide protection against certain types of loss. The fee or premium covers the losses and also the costs of operating the business and earning a profit.

The table on the following page shows types of insurance you can buy to manage different types of risk. Study the table and answer the questions that follow.

NAME: _____ CLASS PERIOD: _____

Types of Insurance

Type of Insurance	Purpose	Examples of Coverage
AUTO	Provides financial protection against losses caused by an auto accident or other damage to a car	**Collision:** Provides for the repair or replacement of the policy owner's car damaged in an accident. **Liability:** Covers the cost of property damage or injuries to others caused by the policy owner. **Comprehensive:** Covers the cost of damage to an automobile as a result of fire, theft, or storms. **Uninsured and underinsured motorist:** Covers the cost of property damage or injuries to the policy holder when the driver at fault is uninsured or doesn't have sufficient coverage to pay for all the expenses related to the accident.
HEALTH	Provides payment for certain health-care costs including coverage for dental and vision care	**Traditional health insurance:** Provides reimbursement for hospital, surgical, medical, and other expenses; plans can include deductible and co-payments of 20 percent or more. **HMOs:** Cover hospital, surgical, and medical services through a group of physicians; fees based on a monthly charge whether or not services are used. **High deductible health care:** Covers hospital, surgical, and medical services through either an HMO or traditional health care plan; consumers pay much higher deductibles in exchange for lower premiums; these policies are often used to insure against catastrophic health events. **Health savings accounts (HSAs):** Provide a tax-sheltered account where consumers can save for their medical expenses.
RENTER'S	Provides financial protection in case of loss of personal possessions in a rental unit, as well as injury to others on the property	Reimburses the policy owner for loss of possessions in a rental unit caused by fire, theft, water damage, etc. Also provides liability protection for bodily injuries occurring in the rental unit.

Type of Insurance	Purpose	Examples of Coverage
HOMEOWNER'S	Protects against financial loss from damage to your home or its contents, as well as injury to others on the property	**Physical damage:** Reimburses for fire or water damage to the house, its contents, or other structures on the property. **Loss or theft:** Reimburses for personal property damaged or stolen. **Liability:** Protects against loss from a lawsuit for injuries to invited or uninvited guests.
LIFE	Provides financial protection to dependents of policy owner when policy owner dies (to cover such expenses as income replacement, debt repayment, funeral expenses, and education expenses)	**Term life:** Offers protection for a specified period of time; the policy must be renewed if coverage is desired for another period of time. **Cash value life:** Combines protection and savings or investment. Cash value life insurance can cost many times more than term life insurance because of the investment feature. However, there are usually many better investment opportunities than cash value insurance. Common types of cash value insurance policies include: • **Whole life:** Provides cash value and protection during the lifetime of the policy holder. • **Universal life:** Provides term policy protection with an investment feature of a whole life policy; the face value of the policy can change during the time of the policy. • **Variable life:** Similar to universal life, but allows the policyholder some choice in the investments for the cash-value portion of the policy.
DISABILITY	Provides income over a specified period when a person is ill and unable to work; most disability policies end at retirement age of 65-70	Policy owner selects a replacement income for lost wages if an illness or accident prevents the person from working. Disability is paid for a specified time after a waiting period. Disability insurance is more important for a young, single person than life insurance. The likelihood that a person in his or her 20s will become disabled is seven times greater than his or her chance of dying.

Questions:

a. All choices involve at least some measure of risk. Name two ways to reduce risks.

b. How does insurance work?

c. What is a premium?

d. What does each type of insurance typically provide?

    i.   Auto:

    ii.   Health:

    iii.   Renter's:

    iv.   Homeowner's:

    v.   Life:

    vi.   Disability:

e. In the case of auto insurance, what is the difference between collision and liability coverage?

f. You are taking a new job and have two choices of health insurance (see below). Which one would you choose and why?

- Traditional health insurance with coverage for office visits, laboratory, hospital costs, and routine care as well as protection for larger bills from illness or injury. The annual deductible is $500, and there is an 80/20 percent co-insurance clause with an out-of-pocket annual limit of $2,000 (this means you are responsible for the first $500 of health expenditures each year and after that, you pay 20% of all medical bills up to a total of $2,000 per year). The monthly premium for this coverage is $180 per month. This plan allows the consumer to use the provider (doctor) of their choice.

- HMO with coverage for all medical expenses. There are no deductibles, but there is a $25 co-pay for each time you visit the doctor. The premium for this coverage is $150 per month. Consumers must use providers within the HMO network to receive services covered by the plan.

NAME: _____ CLASS PERIOD: _____

The Big Risk

You have just graduated from high school or college, and you are single. You own a number of assets that you are thinking of insuring, including an automobile, inherited jewelry, a rare coin set, and the contents of your rented apartment.

Your employer provides a health insurance plan you can purchase. Examine the cost and the risk of each of the things you would like to insure below, and circle them. Do not spend more than $2,900; you may spend less. Indicate your choices below.

Renter's Insurance (theft, fire, acts of nature, liability)		**Jewelry Insurance**		**Automobile Insurance** (collision, comprehensive, liability, uninsured motorist)	
Premium:	$240/year	Premium:	$60/year	Premium:	$1,200/year
Loss:	$2,800	Loss:	$3,400	Loss:	$5,000
Risk:	1 in 12	Risk:	1 in 12	Risk:	8 in 12
Card:	9	Card:	7	Card:	5-12
Deductible:	$250	Deductible:	None	Deductible:	$250
Health Insurance (doctor visits, surgery, lab work)		**Life Insurance** (death, debt repayment, school)		**Rare Coin Insurance** (loss due to theft)	
Premium:	$750/year	Premium:	$300/year	Premium:	$200/year
Loss:	$1,200	Loss:	$300,000	Loss:	$1,000
Risk:	11 in 12	Risk:	1 in 144	Risk:	1 in 12
Card:	2-12	Card:	Must draw two 12s in a row	Card:	4
Co-pay	$25			Deductible:	None
(Assumes 2 visits per year)		Deductible:	None		
Disability Insurance (long-term injury, illness)		**Choices** (types of insurance chosen)		**Premiums**	
Premium:	$700/year				
Loss:	$14,400				
Risk:	7 in 12				
Card:	6-12				
Deductible:	None				

EXERCISE 10.2

Adding Up Insurance

1 Card Chosen	2 Year	3 Annual Premium of Insurance Coverages You Chose	4 Losses Caused by Unexpected Events When Insured (Deductibles, Co-Pay)	5 Losses Caused by Unexpected Events When Uninsured	6 Total Dollar Costs
6	0 (uninsured)	0		$20,600	$20,600
6	0	$1,900 ($1,200 car insurance + $700 disability insurance)	$250 (automobile deductible) $0 (disability)	$1,200 (health)	$3,350
	1 (uninsured)				
	2 (uninsured)				
	3 (uninsured)				
	4 (uninsured)				
	5 (uninsured)				
	1				
	2				
	3				
	4				
	5				

TOTAL (uninsured): _____   TOTAL (insured): _____

Questions:

a. For insured people: What were your losses over the period of the simulation?

b. For uninsured people: What were your losses over the period of the simulation?

c. Which students had fewer losses?

d. Were the costs of purchasing insurance worth the benefits?

Introduction

Spending and Credit

Just about every adult in America uses credit. The Federal Reserve Board's Survey of Consumer Finances provides some interesting figures for U.S. household uses of one form of credit: credit cards. In 2007, 73 percent of all households in the United States had a credit card, but only 46 percent of households carried a balance from one month to the next. Many families use these cards as a convenience and pay their balances off each month.

For those U.S. households maintaining a balance on their credit cards, the median amount owed in 2007 was $3,000. Median figures mean that half of the households had more debt and half had less. On the other hand, the Federal Reserve Board reports that, for households maintaining balances on their credit cards, the average balance was much higher: $7,300.

Some people are afraid of using credit. "Neither a borrower nor a lender be" is an old adage such people might quote. Other people are fearless about using credit, especially credit cards. They might say, "Hey, it's only plastic! Let's go for it!"

There are problems with both viewpoints. Used in a smart way, credit can be a tremendous help to you now and in the future. Used in a stupid way, credit can result in harassment from creditors, broken relationships, and bankruptcy.

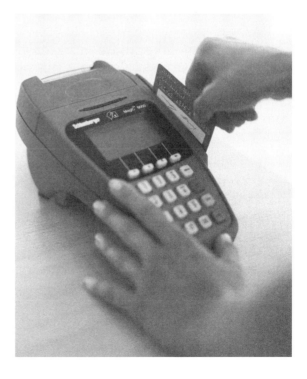

What is credit? Credit means obtaining the use of money that you do not have. To obtain credit, you must convince someone else (usually a financial institution like a bank, savings and loan, credit union, or a credit card company) to provide a loan to you in return for your promise to pay the borrowed money back later, plus an additional charge called interest.

Can using credit help you? You bet! But loans have to be repaid. Lenders charge interest for the use of their money. As people pay off their loans, plus interest, the money that goes for repayment is money they do not have for spending on things they may wish to have today.

Credit that is used unwisely can harm you financially, but you should not be afraid of using credit if you understand the basics. The key is to be smart about the use of credit.

What do lenders look for when they approve a loan to an individual? Ordinarily, they look for the "Three Cs":

- **Character:** Will the applicant be responsible and repay the loan? Your history of credit use is stored in your credit report. Credit reporting agencies use a scoring formula to summarize your creditworthiness. This number is your credit score. Credit scores are used by lenders to determine whether or not you qualify for loans; credit scores also determine in part the interest rate you will be offered. Insurance companies use credit scores in determining how risky you are to insure. Landlords use credit scores in their tenant-screening process. Some employers use credit scores in their evaluation of job candidates.

- **Capacity:** Does the applicant have enough income to comfortably make the payments on the loan amount requested?

- **Collateral:** Will the loan be secured, or guaranteed, by collateral that can be used to repay the debt in case the borrower defaults on the loan?

Consumers sometimes make mistakes in using credit. They are not perfect. People in the lending business also make mistakes. They are not perfect either. The world of finance can be complicated. Some business people take advantage of consumers. Several state and federal laws are designed to protect credit consumers from dishonest business practices. Among the more important consumer-credit protection laws are the Truth in Lending Act and the Fair Credit Reporting Act.

And then there are the scheme artists and swindlers. Unfortunately, the credit and finance industry sometimes attracts unsavory sorts who prey on people's greed or financial fears. If you receive a phone call describing a fantastic loan and a debt repayment plan that sounds too good to be true, it probably is. Hang up the phone. And try to avoid businesses that provide financial services but at very high costs—such as payday loans and rent-to-own plans.

NAME: _____ CLASS PERIOD: _____

What Is Credit?

Credit allows people to obtain the use of money that they do not have. To obtain credit, a prospective borrower must convince someone else (a lender) to provide a loan in return for the borrower's promise to pay the money back, plus an additional charge called interest. People obtain loans to buy cars, homes, and major appliances, to improve their homes, to pay for college education, and so forth.

Credit decisions—whether to borrow money, and for what reasons—can be difficult. Like all difficult decisions, credit decisions involve examining the advantages and disadvantages facing the individual making the choice. The hard part, of course, is figuring out whether the advantages of using credit outweigh the disadvantages.

There are many advantages to using credit. Credit can help people acquire assets. Assets are goods or services that usually retain or increase their value. Ordinarily, a home or post-secondary education is considered an asset. Credit also can help people lead happier lives by enabling them to obtain the goods and services they wish to have now while paying for them in the future. And credit can help people in an emergency.

There are also disadvantages to using credit. Some people make the mistakes of using too much credit in relation to their income; they may then incur heavy burdens of debt from which it is difficult to recover. Many new college graduates, for example, spend a lot of the income from their first jobs repaying large credit card debts they have rolled up while in college. As they spend a great deal of their current income paying for previous purchases, they are left with less money to buy things they would like to have in the present. And if they miss payments or default on loans altogether, they may face serious negative consequences, including the inability to get credit at a later time when it would otherwise make sense to borrow money for a major purchase.

Financial institutions (commercial banks, savings and loans, credit unions, and consumer finance companies) hold money that they, in turn, lend out to others. The owners of financial institutions expect to be compensated when they make a loan. This compensation is called interest. Interest is the price a borrower pays to a lender for use of the credit provided by the lender. Interest is the reward lenders receive for allowing others to use their funds.

Both sides in a credit transaction expect to benefit. Borrowers are able to purchase something that may be of value to them today and/or in the future. Lenders are repaid the money that they lent, plus interest.

An important factor in determining the rate of interest to be charged is the amount of confidence the lender has that the amount of the loan, plus interest, will be repaid in the agreed-upon time. Higher-risk loans—loans where it is uncertain that the borrower can repay—usually result in higher interest rates. Lower-risk loans—loans where it seems evident that the borrower can repay—usually result in lower interest rates.

A loan for an intangible item, like a vacation, is likely to cost more in interest than a loan for a tangible item, like a home. Secured loans (those that are backed by other assets, like your home or your car), are likely to have lower interest rates than unsecured loans (those that are not backed by other assets). An asset used to back a loan is called collateral.

Questions:

a. Why use credit?

b. What are the advantages of using credit?

c. What are the disadvantages of using credit?

d. What institutions are sources of credit?

e. What is interest?

f. Who most often wins in a credit transaction?

g. How does risk influence the rate of interest?

h. What is an unsecured loan?

i. What is collateral?

NAME: _____ CLASS PERIOD: _____

Common Forms of Credit

Types of Credit	Lender	Advantages	Disadvantages
Home Mortgage	• Commercial bank • Savings and loan • Credit union • Consumer finance company	• Homes can increase in value. • Interest rates for mortgage are relatively low. • The interest paid is tax-deductible.	• Mortgages are usually long-term commitments. • Obtaining a home loan involves extensive credit checks.
Car Loans	• Commercial bank • Savings and loan • Credit union • Consumer finance company	• Cars can make it easier to work and earn an income.	• Cars lose their value relatively quickly. The car you purchase on credit may have little value when the last payment is made.
College Loans	• Commercial bank • Credit union • Savings and loan associations	• A college education is usually a good investment.	• Students sometimes borrow more than is necessary. • New graduates can face difficulty in repaying large loans.
Personal Loans	• Commercial bank • Savings and loan • Credit union • Consumer finance company	• Personal loans allow individuals to purchase today that boat or vacation they want.	• Personal loans have relatively high interest rates. • Some people may borrow more than their income should allow.
Credit Cards	• Commercial bank • Savings and loan • Department stores • Other financial institutions • Credit union	• Credit cards are convenient to use and useful in an emergency. • Credit cards provide a record of charges.	• Credit cards may have relatively high interest rates. • Some card holders may borrow more than their income should allow.

Questions:

a. What are the advantages of home loans and college loans compared to credit card and personal loans?

b. What are the disadvantages of credit cards and college loans?

NAME: _____ CLASS PERIOD: _____

Credit Research

Directions: Outside of class, identify one example of each of the four types of financial institutions listed below. Try to find examples from within your community. As necessary, look beyond your community by using the Internet. After you have identified the four examples, get in touch with a representative from each one. You may do this by telephone, in person, or via the Internet. Ask each representative what the current annual percentage rate (APR) is, at his or her institution, for each of the five types of loans listed. The APR is the best way to compare the cost of credit from one lender to another. Record the information in the correct places on the chart and report the results to class.

Credit Research Results

Loans	APR for a 4-year car loan	APR for a college loan	APR for a 30-year home mortgage	APR for a credit card	APR for a personal loan to pay for a vacation
Institutions					
Commercial Bank					
Savings and Loan					
Credit Union					
Consumer Finance Company					

Questions:

a. Which local institutions offered the best APR for each type of loan?

b. Which local institutions offered the highest APR for each type of loan?

c. How did the loans from online lenders compare to loans from lenders in your community?

NAME: _____ CLASS PERIOD: _____

Sharp Financial Advisors

Part 1: Your Job

You run a small consulting business, giving advice to people who are thinking about applying for credit. For a small fee, you offer your customers advice on whether they should apply for a loan. Your business has been successful because you understand the advantages and disadvantages of using various forms of credit. You ask your clients what is most important to their future success, and you compare the advantages of using credit to the disadvantages of using credit, according to the following general principles.

Advantages of using credit:

- Credit can help people acquire valuable assets.
- Credit can help people lead happier lives.
- Credit can help people in an emergency.

Disadvantages of using credit:

- People may use too much credit in relation to their income.
- Credit requires borrowers to pay interest to lenders; interest payments leave borrowers with less money to spend on things they may want to have now and until the loan is paid off.
- Misusing credit can put borrowers at a disadvantage, threatening their ability to qualify for loans in the future or requiring them to pay higher rates of interest on loans they may obtain in the future.

Bearing these general principles in mind, read the four cases described on the next two pages. After reading each client's case, answer the questions that follow.

Part 2: The Four Cases

Client 1

I am 17 years old and a high school senior. I have earned good grades in high school. I have been admitted to a good state university. I would like to go to college full-time and work only a few hours a week. With this schedule, I think that I can complete my college degree in four years. I am planning to major in chemical engineering. My college advisor has told me that chemical engineering is a hard major. My parents have no money to support me in college. I am planning to apply for aid and to use college loans to pay for my college tuition and books. I plan to live at home and work in the summer to earn spending money for use during the school year. I will be borrowing about $50,000 in total. Should I apply for the loan?

a. What is the main advantage of getting credit in this case?

b. What is the main disadvantage of getting credit?

c. Is the loan being used to purchase a valuable asset?

d. Do you think the client is likely to be able to repay the loan?

e. Do you recommend that this client apply for the loan? Explain.

Client 2

I am 18 years old. I attend the local vocational-technical school. My area of study is commercial heating and cooling. My school tuition is relatively low and I will complete my program of study in nine months. I can pay most of my expenses by working full-time in the summer and part-time during the school year. I am still living at home, and I plan to get an apartment of my own next year. I am an avid sports fan. I have a little 12-inch television set in my room. I'd like to use my credit card to buy a flat screen 38-inch television set at a cost of $1,300.

a. What is the main advantage of getting credit in this case?

b. What is the main disadvantage of getting credit?

c. Is the loan being used to purchase a valuable asset?

d. Do you think the client is likely to be able to repay the loan?

e. Do you recommend that this client apply for the loan? Explain.

Client 3

I am 21 years old and finishing my last year in college. I have been studying hard and have earned relatively good grades. My major is English. A small group of my friends want to bust out for spring break and take a one-week vacation in Florida. I have never really had a vacation while in college except for two trips with my family. If I book my reservations now, I can get relatively low air fare and hotel rates. In all, the trip will cost me about $1,500. I am a little low on cash. I am planning to charge the $1,500 on my credit card.

a. What is the main advantage of getting credit in this case?

b. What is the main disadvantage of getting credit?

c. Is the loan being used to purchase a valuable asset?

d. Do you think the client is likely to be able to repay the loan?

e. Do you recommend that this client apply for the loan? Explain.

Client 4

I am 22 years old. I am just about to complete a two-year dental hygienist program at a local vocational school. My first-year pay will be about $25,000 plus fringe benefits including health insurance and a 401k program. My workplace is 20 miles from my apartment and is not on a city bus route. The car I have has 225,000 miles on the odometer, and it burns more oil than gas. Yesterday, I noticed that I can see the road through a hole in the floor in front of the driver's seat! I have saved $2,000 for a down payment on a new car, but I will need to borrow several thousand more to buy a new car that is fuel-efficient and dependable.

a. What is the main advantage of getting credit in this case?

b. What is the main disadvantage of getting credit?

c. Is the loan being used to purchase a valuable asset?

d. Do you think the client is likely to be able to repay the loan?

e. Do you recommend that this client apply for the loan? Explain.

NAME: _____ CLASS PERIOD: _____

Reading a Credit Report

Your ability to qualify for a loan depends on a credit report. A credit report is a record of an individual's personal credit history. It is probably a good indicator of the applicant's character and whether he or she will repay borrowed money as agreed.

When someone applies for a loan, the lender will order a credit report to see how well the applicant has managed credit in the past. A credit report will tell, in detail, how much the person has borrowed, from whom, and whether the bills have been paid on time.

Credit reports are compiled by credit bureaus, which regularly collect information on millions of consumers. Credit bureaus get information from a variety of sources, including stores, credit card companies, banks, mortgage companies, and medical providers. When you fill out an application for credit, the information on that application is also sent to a credit bureau.

What Are Lenders Looking For?

Lenders look for certain qualities in loan applicants. These qualities are called the 3 Cs of Credit: capacity, character, and collateral. A discussion of each follows.

Capacity: Capacity refers to the loan applicant's ability to repay the debt in question. The basic question is "Have you been working regularly in an occupation that is likely to provide enough income to support your use of credit?" More particular questions might address the following:

- ✔ Do you have a steady job?
- ✔ What is your salary?
- ✔ How reliable is your income?
- ✔ Do you have other sources of income?
- ✔ How many other loan payments do you have?
- ✔ What are your current debts?
- ✔ Do you pay alimony or child support?
- ✔ Can you afford your lifestyle?

Character: Questions will be asked to determine whether you are honest and reliable—thus likely to pay debts. Here are some examples:

✔ Have you used credit before?

✔ Do you pay your bills on time?

✔ Do you have a good credit report?

✔ Can you provide character references?

✔ How long have you lived at your present address?

✔ How long have you been at your present job?

Collateral: Collateral refers to assets that could be sold to pay off your loan in the event that you could not do so. Collateral serves as a type of insurance for the creditor. Questions related to collateral may include the following:

✔ Do you have a checking account?

✔ Do you have a savings account?

✔ Do you own any stocks or bonds?

✔ Do you have any valuable collections or jewelry?

✔ Do you own your own home?

✔ Do you own a car?

✔ Do you own a boat?

The Importance of a Good Credit Rating

A *good* rating on a credit report means that, in the past, bills have been paid on time.

A *poor* rating indicates overdue payments or bills that have gone unpaid.

It is extremely important to build and maintain a good credit history. A good credit report can often make the difference between getting a loan or being turned down. In addition, potential employers and landlords will often check an applicant's credit report before making a final decision about offering a job or a renting out an apartment.

Credit Reports May Contain Errors

Mistakes can and do sometimes occur on credit reports. For example, a credit report may contain information about a different person with the same name as the applicant, or paid accounts may be listed incorrectly as unpaid. The law provides individuals with a means of requesting and reviewing their credit reports and having mistakes corrected. Under the Fair and Accurate Credit Transactions Act you have the right to get a free copy of your credit report from each credit bureau annually. The official site established by the three credit reporting agencies for free reports is www.annualcreditreport.com. The Fair Credit Reporting Act allows you to receive a free copy of your credit report if you are turned down for credit or are the victim of identity theft. The three largest credit bureaus are:

✔ Equifax

✔ Experian

✔ TransUnion

What's My Score?

Credit reporting agencies summarize much of the information in your credit report into one credit score. The formula for computing credit scores was developed by Fair Isaac Corporation; the scores are commonly referred to as FICO scores. The scores range from 300 to 850, with the median score being 723. People with lower scores are more likely to be denied credit or charged higher interest rates. People with scores of 770 or higher will receive the best rates for loans. Scores of 640 or more will qualify applicants for fairly good rates. People with scores of 600 or less will have difficulty getting a loan. These people probably need credit counseling.

The following chart shows how lenders use FICO scores to evaluate loan applicants. For example, the chart shows that 8 percent of borrowers had FICO scores of 550 to 599, and approximately half of them either didn't pay back money they owed or were more than 90 days late in making their payments. In contrast, 27 percent of borrowers have a score of 750 to 799, and only 2 percent of them were delinquent.

FICO Scores: Measure Credit Risk

How Borrowers Rank		Delinquency Rates by FICO Scores	
Up to 499	2%	Up to 499	87%
500 to 549	5%	500 to 549	71%
550 to 599	8%	550 to 599	51%
600 to 649	12%	600 to 649	31%
650 to 699	15%	650 to 699	15%
700 to 749	18%	700 to 749	5%
750 to 799	27%	750 to 799	2%
800 +	13%	800 +	1%

Source: Fair Isaac

Who Uses Credit Scores?

Lenders aren't the only ones who use credit scores. Insurance companies use them in their evaluations of a new client's risk. A person with a low credit score may not be able to buy insurance, or will be charged a higher premium. Landlords also request credit scores when evaluating new tenants. People who have difficulty paying their bills may not be able to pay their rent on time. Finally, some employers use credit scores when screening new applicants for jobs. Employers seeking to fill jobs which require the handling of cash, or jobs paying salaries over $100,000, are especially likely to request a credit score for the applicant.

What Information Is Used to Calculate My Score?

- **Payment history (35%)**

  The most important part of a credit score is your repayment history. More than a third of your score is based on whether or not you have paid your bills and whether you have paid them on time. Most people are never late in paying their bills. So, if you are ever a late payer, even a few times, it will hurt your score.

  How late you are (whether it's 30, 60, or 90 days) makes a difference, too. An account that was late 90 days or never repaid will hurt your score more than one that was late 30 days.

- **Amounts owed (30%)**

  The second most important factor is the amount of debt you currently owe. This measure is based on your current level of debt compared to your income. It also includes a measure of how much credit you are currently using out of the amount of credit that is available to you. Many lenders will not make loans to individuals who are already spending 25 percent of their gross income to repay debt. They feel that the borrower will not have enough discretionary income to make additional payments, reliably, on a new loan. For example: A person who owes money on school loans, a car loan, a mortgage, and lots of credit card payments, totaling 50 percent of his or her take-home pay, probably wouldn't be able to handle any more debt.

  In addition to the actual amount of debt you currently owe, lenders will look at how you are currently using of the credit available to you. If you have two credit cards with a total credit limit of $10,000 and a balance of $5,000 (a ratio of 5,000/10,000 or 50%) you will be more likely to qualify for a loan than someone who has a $1,000 credit limit with a balance of $900 (900/1,000 or a ratio of 90%).

- **Length of credit history (15%)**

  The length of time that you have had credit affects your credit score. Sometimes people are encouraged to keep old accounts open with no balance just to help their credit score.

- **Types of credit (10%)**
  Lenders like to see a mix of installment loans and credit cards. However, it is much more important to pay all of your bills on time than to have variety in your credit profile.

- **New credit and inquiries (10%)**
  Each time you apply for credit, the lender will request your credit report. These requests, sometimes called inquiries, temporarily reduce your credit score. Applications for new credit following recent late payments are viewed more negatively because they are seen as a sign that you are trying to borrow to pay current debt rather than to buy a new asset.

  However, there may be times—when you are shopping for a car, perhaps—when you will apply for credit at several places during a short period of time (say, 30 days) to see where you can get the best offer for a loan. These inquiries are viewed differently; they don't affect your credit score as negatively as several independent credit applications throughout the year.

  What can you do to earn a good credit score or improve your score? Pay your bills on time and limit the amount of debt you take on. These two factors account for 65 percent of your credit score!

Ways to Establish and Keep a Good Credit History and Improve Your Credit Score

There are several steps you can take to establish and maintain a good credit history.

- ✔ Always pay your bills on time.
- ✔ Never borrow more than you can comfortably pay back.
- ✔ Borrow only the amount you need.
- ✔ Know how much you owe at all times.
- ✔ Contact lenders immediately if you expect to have a payment problem.
- ✔ Develop good saving habits so that you can handle financial emergencies without borrowing.
- ✔ Report lost or stolen credit cards immediately.
- ✔ Never give your credit card number or other personal information over the phone or on the Internet unless you initiated the transaction.
- ✔ Open a checking account and a savings account.
- ✔ Do not apply for too many credit cards. Even if you don't use them, the credit limits are taken into consideration when you apply for credit.

EXERCISE 13.1

Questions:

a. What are the "3 Cs of Credit"?

b. Give examples of each of the 3 Cs of Credit.

c. What is a credit report?

d. Why should a person care about his or her credit report?

e. Are you allowed to check the accuracy of your credit report?

f. Is there a charge for checking the accuracy of your credit report?

g. What is a credit score?

NAME: _____ CLASS PERIOD: _____

Evaluating a Credit Report

Study the credit report on the following pages and answer the questions below.

Questions:

a. Whose credit report is this?

b. How many potentially negative items are listed?

c. How many accounts are in good standing?

d. On page 2, there are two very negative items. What are they?

_____   _____

e. Have any of John Q. Consumer's credit cards been lost or stolen?

f. Does John Q. Consumer have a good credit record with First Credit Union and National Credit Card? What are the reasons for your opinion?

g. Who requested John Q. Consumer's credit report in 2009?

_____   _____

_____

h. Is John Q. Consumer a homeowner?

i. What is the most negative item on this report, and for how many years does that item remain in the credit report?

j. What is John Q. Consumer's credit score?

k. If you were a lender, would you grant John Q. Consumer credit? Why or why not?

Credit Report of John Q. Consumer

Credit R Us

Prepared for
John Q. Consumer

Report number
1687771839-0000051088

Report date
June 01, 2009

Page 1 of 7

Personal Credit Report

About this report
Credit R Us collects and organizes information about you and your credit history from public records, your creditors, and other reliable sources. We make your credit history available to your current and prospective creditors and employers as allowed by law. We do not grant credit or evaluate your credit history. Personal data about you may be made available to companies whose products and services interest you.

Important decisions about your creditworthiness are based on the information in this report. You should review it carefully for accuracy.

Report number
Below is a summary of the information contained in this report.

Potentially negative items listed

Public records   2
Accounts with creditors and others   2

Accounts in good standing   3

Credit Score   550

Credit R Us
P.O. Box 9595
Allen TX 75013-9595

If you have questions
For all questions about this report, please call us at:
1-888-000-0000
M - F 7:30am – 7:00 pm CT

To learn more about Credit R Us or for other helpful information, including tips on how to improve your creditworthiness, visit our web site:
http://www.creditrus.com

Credit R Us

Prepared for
John Q. Consumer

Report number
1687771839-0000051088

Report date
June 01, 2009

Page 2 of 7

Information affecting your creditworthiness

Items listed with dashes before and after the number, for example –1–, may potentially have a negative effect on your future credit extension and are listed first on the report.

Credit grantors may carefully review the items listed below when they check your credit history. Please note that the account information connected with some public records, such as bankruptcy, also may appear with your credit accounts listed later in this report.

Important decisions about your creditworthiness are based on the information in this report. You should review it carefully for accuracy.

Your statement

At your request, we've included the following statement every time your credit report is requested.

"My identification has been used without my consent on applications for credit. Please call me at 999.999.9999 before approving credit in my name."

Public record information about you

Source/ Identification number	Location number	Date filed/ Date resolved	Responsibility	Claim amount Liability amount	Comments
-1- HOLLY COW DIST CT 305 MAIN STREET HOLLY NJ 08060	B312P7659	3-2005/NA	Joint	$3,765/NA	Status: civil claim judgement filed. Plaintiff: Dime Savings. This item is scheduled to continue on record until 3-2012. This item was verified on 8-2005 and remained unchanged.
-2- BROWN TOWN HALL 10 COURT STREET BROWN NJ 02809	Bk443PG14	11-2005/NA	Joint	$57,786/NA	Status: chapter 7 bankruptcy discharged. This item is scheduled to continue on record until 11-2015. This item was verified on 8-2005 and remained unchanged.

Credit R Us

Prepared for
John Q. Consumer

Report number
1687771839-0000051088

Report date
June 01, 2009

Page 3 of 7

Credit information about you

Source/Account number (except last few digits)	Date opened/ Reported since	Date of status/ Last reported	Type/Terms/ Monthly payments	Responsibility	Credit limit or original amount/ High balance	Recent balance/ Recent payment	Comments
-3- FIDELITY BK NA 300 FIDELITY PLAZA NORTHSHORE NJ 08902 46575000024	6-2002/ 6-2002	12-2004/ 12-2004	Installment/ 10 months/$0	Individual	$4,549/NA	$4,549 as of 12-2004	Status: Charge off. $4,549 written off in 12-2004. This account is scheduled to continue until 12-2011.
-4- B.B. Credit 35 WASHINGTON ST. DEDHAM MA 547631236	10-1998/ 4-2003	4-2006/ 4-2006	Installment/ 80 months/$34	Individual	$8,500/$8,500	$0 as of 4-2006/ $34	Status: Debt reincluded in chapter 7 bankruptcy. $389 written off in 3-2006. Account history: Collection as of 9-2003 thru 6-2004 90 days as of 7-2003 60 days as of 11-2002, 6-2003. 30 days as of 9-2002, 1-2003 and 2 other times. This account is scheduled to continue on record until 2-2009. This item was verified and updated on 6-2004.

Credit R Us

Prepared for
John Q. Consumer

Report number
1687771839-0000051088

Report date
June 01, 2009

Page 4 of 7

Credit information about you *continued*

Source/Account number (except last few digits)	Date opened/ Reported since	Date of status/ Last reported	Type/Terms/ Monthly payments	Responsibility	Credit limit or original amount/ High balance	Recent balance/ Recent payment	Comments
5 FIRST CREDIT UNION 748 WASHINGTON LNE LANEVILLE TX 76362 129474 Mortgage: 74848347834	3-2004/ 3-2004	11-2006/ 11-2006	Installment/ 48 Months/$420		$17,856/NA	$0 as of 11-2006/ $420	Status: open/never late.
6 AMERICAN FINANCE CORP PO BOX 8633 COLLEY IL 60126 6376001172...	6-2001/ 7-2001	11-2006/ 11-2006	Revolving/NA $400		$18,251	$0 as of 11-2006	Status: card reported lost or stolen. This account is scheduled to continue on record until 11-2009.
7 NATIONAL CREDIT CARD 100 THE PLAZA LAKEVILLE NJ 08905 420000638...	6-2001/ 6-2001	11-2006/ 11-2006	Revolving/NA/ $0	Joint with JANE CONSUMER	$8,000 $8,569	$0 as of 11-2006	Status: open/never late.

Credit R Us

Prepared for
John Q. Consumer

Report number
1687771839-0000051088

Report date
June 01, 2009

Page 5 of 7

Your use of credit

The information listed below provides additional detail about your accounts, showing up to 24 months of balance history, your credit limit, high balance or original loan amount. Not all balance history is reported to Credit R Us, so some of your accounts may not appear. Also, some credit grantors may update the information more than once in the same month.

Source/Account number	Date/Balance						
6 AMERICAN FINANCE CORP. 6376001172	11-2006/$0	10-2006/$4,329	8-2006/$0	5-2006/$0	2-2006/$250	1-2006/$0	12-2005/$2,951
	9-2005/$3,451	7-2005/$4,251	5-2005/$4,651	2-2005/$5,451	1-2005/$5,851;	12-2004/$6,251	
	11-2004/$6,651	9-2004/$7,051	7-2004/$7,451	5-2004/$7,852	3-2004/$8,251	1-2004/$12,651	
	12-2003/$9,051	11-2003/$9,451	9-2003/$10,251	7-2003/$10,651	5-2003/$11,051		
Between 1-2002 and 11-2006 your credit limit was unknown.							
7 NATIONAL CREDIT CARD 420000638	11-2006/$0	9-2006/$542	7-2006/$300	6-2006/$686	4-2006/$1,400	3-2006/$2,500	1-2006/$2,774
	12-2005/$599	9-2005/$873	7-2005/$1,413	5-2005/$1,765	4-2005/$2,387	3-2005/$3,400	
	2-2005/$3,212	1-2005/$4,412	12-2004/$2,453	9-2004/$2,453	10-2004/$1,769	8-2004/$1,200	
	4-2004/$3,200	2-2004/$4,568	1-2004/$5,582	12-2003/$3,000	10-2003/$3,200	8-2003/$4,500	
Between 6-2001 and 11-2006 your credit limit was $8,000.							

Credit R Us

Prepared for
John Q. Consumer

Report number
1687771839-0000051088

Report date
June 01, 2009

Page 6 of 7

Others who have requested your credit history
Listed below are all those who have received information from us in the recent past about your credit history.

Requests initiated by you
You took actions, such as completing a credit application that allowed the following sources to review your information. Please note that the following information is part of your credit history and is included in our reports to others.

Source	Date	Comments
ABC MORTGAGE 64 MAPLE ROSEVILLE, MD 02849	10-18-2006	Real estate loan of $214,000 on behalf of State Bank with 30 year repayment terms. This inquiry is scheduled to continue on record until 10-2009.

Other requests
You may not have initiated the following requests for your credit history, so you may not recognize each source. We offer credit information about you to those with a permissible purpose, for example, to:

- other creditors who want to offer you pre-approved credit;
- an employer who wishes to extend an offer of employment;
- a potential investor in assessing the risk of a current obligation;
- Credit R Us Customers Assistance to process a report for you;
- your current creditors to monitor your accounts (date listed may affect only the most recent request).

We report these requests **only** to you as a record of activities, and we do not include **any** of these requests on credit reports to others.

Source	Date
CREDIT R US PO BOX 949 ALLEN TX 75013	3-09
WORLD BANK PO BOX 949 ALLEN TX 75013	3-09, 12-08, 9-08, 6-08, 3-08, 12-07, 9-07, 6-07, 3-07
FIDELITY BK NA 300 FIDELITY PLAZA NORTHSHORE NJ 08902	1-09, 7-08, 1-08, 7-07, 1-07
NATIONAL CREDIT REPORT 100 THE PLAZA LANEVILLE NJ 08905	7-07, 2-07

Credit R Us

Prepared for
John Q. Consumer

Report number
1687771839-0000051088

Report date
June 01, 2009

Page 7 of 7

Personal information about you
The following information associated with your records has been reported to us by you, your creditors, and other sources. As part of our fraud-prevention program, a notice with additional information may appear in your report.

Names
John Q. Consumer

Residences
Our records show you currently are a homeowner. The geographical code shown with each address identifies the state, country, census tract, block group, and Metropolitan Statistical Area associated with each address.

Address	Type of address	Geographical code
7972 PADDOCK CT LANEVILLE, TX 00000	Single Family	0-192053-3-0
1777 BEVERLY AVE SOMEWHERE, NJ 00000	Single Family	0-224681-25-0
250 GARDEN DRIVE ANYWHERE, NJ 00000	Single Family	0-9004-93-0

Social Security number
111-11-1111

Year of birth
1964

Driver's license number
CA X123456

Spouse's name
JANE

Driver's license number
CA X123456

Notices
The first Social Security number listed shows that credit was established before the number was issued.

NAME: _____ CLASS PERIOD: _____

Evaluating Three Loan Applications

Listed below are three loan applicants who are interested in buying a new car. Based solely on the information provided and their credit score, determine whether you would approve or decline their loan requests. There is no specific credit score for which lenders would deny a loan automatically, based only on a score. However, the credit score does provide useful information about the creditworthiness of the individual. If you decide to make a loan to the applicant, assign an interest rate appropriate for the applicant's score. Check your response and then write the reason for your decisions. Interest rates typically assigned to various credit scores are provided on the following page.

Status codes given at the end of the reports.

JANICE BROWN					Credit Score 450	
Company name	Months reviewed	High credit	Terms	Balance	Past due	Status
Sears	2	2,016	24	838		R3
Dept. of Educ.	7	1,507		1,507	158	I5
Dept. of Educ.	2	512		512	512	I5
ABC Credit Card	8	3,000	29	1,363		R1
Record of Month	6			28	38	O3

_____ **Approve** _____ **Decline** _____ **Not Sure** _____ **Interest Rate**

Why?

TITO SANDERS					Credit Score 770	
Company name	Months reviewed	High credit	Terms	Balance	Past due	Status
Hometown Bank	24	11,000	60	5,350		I1
ABC Credit Card	6	2,500	36	0		O0
Dept. of Educ.	5	2,000	24	1,380		I1
XYZ Credit Card	12	3,000	24	495		R1

_____ **Approve** _____ **Decline** _____ **Not Sure** _____ **Interest Rate**

Why?

MARIA MARTINEZ					Credit Score 620	
Company name	Months reviewed	High credit	Terms	Balance	Past due	Status
Hometown Bank	13	7,200	48	5,800		I1
ABC Credit Card	7	2,000	24	488		R1

_____ Approve   _____ Decline   _____ Not Sure   _____ Interest Rate

Why?

Status Codes

Type of account

O = Open

R = Revolving

I = Installment

Timeliness of payment

0 = Approved, not used

1 = Paid as agreed

2 = 30 days past due

3 = 60 days past due

4 = 90 days past due

5 = 120 days past due

7 = Making regular payments under wage earner plan

8 = Repossession

9 = Seriously delinquent/bad debt (paid or unpaid; charged off account)

FICO SCORE	APR
720-850	6.098%
690-719	7.644%
660-689	9.059%
620-659	11.761%
590-619	15.478%
500-589	16.202%

NAME: _____ CLASS PERIOD: _____

Everything You Wanted to Know About Figuring Interest

Credit isn't free. The price of credit is called the interest rate, and total interest paid is known as the finance charge. The finance charge is usually stated in dollars, but sometimes it is stated as a percentage of the loan. When stated as a percentage of the loan, it is another way to refer to the interest rate.

The Truth in Lending Law makes comparing credit costs fairly simple. This federal law requires that all lenders state their finance charges and interest rates in the same way. This rate is called the annual percentage rate, or APR. An APR is the rate you pay in a single year on the money you borrow.

Every loan must also state the finance charge. When stated in dollars, the finance charge is the total dollar amount of interest and other fees you must pay on the loan. The amount you borrow is called the principal of the loan. You pay back the principal plus the finance charge. The finance charge depends on the interest rate, the principal, the loan fees, and the length of the loan. The higher the APR and the longer the period of the loan, the higher the finance charge. By using your math skills, you can save big bucks on a loan. Let's find out how.

Part 1: Figuring Simple Interest

First, let's figure some finance charges. Here is the basic formula for figuring out interest:

$$FC = PRT$$

FC: **Finance charge or total interest**
P: **Principal**
R: **Interest Rate (an add-on rate, expressed in decimal form)**
T: **Time (in years)**

In this formula, the rate is an add-on rate with one payment of principal. An add-on rate is a simplified way to compute total interest on a loan. It is calculated by simply determining the total interest that is payable on the full principal. This amount is then added to the amount of the principal to determine the total amount owed. Note that this is different from calculating payments according to APR procedures.

This formula assumes that the principal (amount of loan) and the interest are paid in one lump sum at the maturity date (end of loan period). For example, if you borrowed $2,000 at a 12 percent add-on rate for two years, the interest would be $480 ($480 = $2,000 x .12 x 2). The amount of $2,480 (interest and principal) would be repaid at the end of two years.

Questions:

a. Gabrielle Daily borrows $1,000 at a 6 percent add-on rate for one year. What is the finance charge?

b. Jesse Candelaria borrows $2,000 at a 10 percent add-on rate for three years. What is the finance charge?

c. Jessica Tate borrows $2,000 at a 10 percent add-on rate for two years. What is the finance charge?

d. Travis Whitaker borrows $2,000 at an 8 percent add-on rate for two years. What is the finance charge?

e. If you want to reduce the finance charge, should you shop for a higher or lower interest rate? Why?

f. If you want to reduce the finance charge, should you pay back the loan more quickly or less quickly? Why?

Part 2: Figuring Monthly Payments

Most loans are paid back on a monthly basis. Very few are paid back all at once at the maturity value of the loan. The monthly payment is the amount the borrower must pay the lender each month to pay back the loan. The monthly payment covers both principal and an interest finance charge. When using add-on interest, the formula for figuring the monthly payment is:

$$MP = \frac{(P + FC)}{N}$$

MP: **Monthly payment**

P: **Principal of the loan**

FC: **Finance charge or total interest**
        (Calculated in the same way as in part 1 above)

N: **Number of months the loan is for**

For example, you borrow $10,000 at an 8 percent add-on rate for four years.

$$P = \$10,000$$
$$FC = (\$10,000 \times .08 \times 4) = \$3,200$$
$$MP = \frac{(\$10,000 + \$3,200)}{48} = \$275$$

Questions:

a. David Kim borrows $8,000 at an 8 percent add-on rate for two years.

   -What is the finance charge?

   -What is the monthly payment?

b. Marcia Torres borrows $8,000 at an 8 percent add-on rate for four years.

   -What is the finance charge?

   -What is the monthly payment?

c. If a borrower takes longer to pay back a loan, what happens to the monthly payment?

d. If a borrower takes longer to pay back a loan, what happens to the finance charge?

e. What are the costs and benefits of taking longer to pay off a loan?

Part 3: Determining the APR

In the past, lenders advertised interest rates in various ways. In some instances, people were paying higher rates than they thought they would pay because lenders were figuring the rates differently. Consumers had difficulty shopping for credit because of these variations in figuring rates.

Let's look at a couple of examples to illustrate what was being done. Suppose George secures a $1,200 loan at 10 percent add-on interest for one year—a loan that he would pay off (interest and principal) at the end of the year. At the end of the year, he would pay $1,320 to the lender ($1,200 principal plus $120 finance charge). The interest rate advertised for this loan was 10 percent.

Now suppose that Sheila secured a $1,200 loan at 10 percent add-on interest, paying $110 a month. She would be paying a total of $1,320 as well. Before the Truth in Lending Law, the lender probably would have advertised this loan as a 10 percent interest loan, just like the lender for George's loan. In reality, are both of them paying the same interest rate?

They are certainly paying the same amount of interest, but they are not paying the same rate of interest. Why? In the first situation, the person receiving the loan has the full $1,200 for the entire year. In the second situation, part of the $110 a month is going toward the repayment of the loan. Sheila has less of the loan each month because of her monthly payments.

The Truth in Lending Law was established so that individuals shopping for credit could have a common basis for comparing loans. According to this law, the interest rate must be stated as an Annual Percentage Rate (APR), based on the declining balance of the loan. The Truth in Lending Law also requires that the full amount of finance charges (interest plus other charges) must be indicated to the consumer.

There can be variations on the formula for determining the effective APR for a loan. One method using simple interest computations is:

$$\text{APR} = \frac{2 \times M \times FC}{P \times (N + 1)}$$

M: **Number of payments per year**
       (For monthly payments this is always 12)

FC: **Finance charge or total interest**

P: **Principal**

N: **Total number of payments**

Let's figure out the APR for Sheila's loan by first looking at the finance charge that she pays.

$$\$120 = \$1,200 \text{ (principal)} \times .10 \text{ (interest rate)} \times 1 \text{ (number of years)}$$

Now let's figure the annual percentage rate using the APR formula.

$$\text{APR} = \frac{2 \times 12 \times \$120}{\$1200 \times 13} = \frac{\$2880}{\$15,600} = 0.1846 = 18.46\%$$

Notice that the APR for Sheila is much higher than the 10 percent that was probably quoted to her by the lender. If you use the formula for George's loan, you will see that it will come out to 10 percent APR since there was no declining balance on the loan. He always had $1,200 available on the loan.

Questions:
Now let's figure some APRs. All these loans are paid back on a monthly basis.

a. Lisa Rosas borrows $5,000 at a 5 percent add-on rate for one year.
   -What is the finance charge?

   -What is the APR?

b. Brett Olson borrows $6,000 for three years at a 7 percent add-on rate.
   -What is the finance charge?

   -What is the APR?

c. What is the relationship between an APR for an add-on rate for a one-payment loan compared to an APR for an add-on rate on a monthly installment loan?

NAME: _____ CLASS PERIOD: _____

Comparing Credit Cards

1. Credit cards are in widespread use

Americans love credit cards. Here are some statistics that show how widespread credit card use is in the United States.

- 73% of all U.S. families had at least one credit card in 2007.

- Most U.S. families do not have credit card debt. In 2007, only 46.1 percent of families carried a credit card balance.

- For those who carry a credit card balance, the median amount owed was $3,000 in 2007.

- For those who carry a credit card balance, the average amount owed was $7,300 in 2007.

- Ninety-six percent of families with credit cards have a bank-type card. Bank cards accounted for 87 percent of all outstanding credit card balances.

- The average family has two bank-type credit cards.

- The median credit limit on bank-type cards was $18,000 in 2007.

- The median interest rate on bank-type cards was 12.5 percent in 2007.

- Credit cards are an important component of all consumer credit in the United States. In 2009, total revolving debt (credit card debt is the majority of this amount) of U.S. households was $866.1 billion.

(These statistics come from Federal Reserve statistical releases and the *Survey of Consumer Finances* conducted by the Federal Reserve in 2007. For more information on the *Survey of Consumer Finances*, see "Changes in U.S. Family Finances from 2004 to 2007: Evidence from the *Survey of Consumer Finances*" by B. K. Bucks, A. B. Kennickell, T. L. Mach, and K. B. Moore, published in the *Federal Reserve Bulletin*, February 2009.)

2. Shopping for a credit card can save you money. Not all credit cards are alike. Here are some ways in which they differ:

- **The annual fee.** Some credit cards charge an annual fee, and some do not. The amount of the annual fee may vary from card to card. Most people who have a strong credit record can find cards that do not charge an annual fee.

- **Other fees.** Credit cards usually charge stated fees for late or missed payments, going over your credit limit, or making certain transactions such as cash advances.

- **The annual percentage rate (APR).** The APR can vary from card to card by several percentage points. Furthermore, some credit cards offer a low APR for the first few months and then increase it after three or six months. The APR on cash advances often differs from the APR for purchases.

- **The grace period.** This is the amount of time a cardholder has to pay the credit card balance without paying interest. The longer the grace period, the more interest-free days the cardholder has. If the entire balance is paid within the grace period, no interest is due.

- **The way interest is figured.** There are many different methods of calculating credit card interest. These include:

  Average daily balance: The interest rate is calculated each day on the average of each day's balance for the billing cycle. This is the most frequently-used method.

  Adjusted balance: The interest rate is calculated on the opening balance after subtracting the payments made during the month.

  Previous balance: Interest is calculated on the opening balance regardless of payments made during the month.

- **The credit limit.** This is the maximum amount of money a cardholder can charge. A higher credit limit gives the cardholder flexibility but can also lead to credit card balances that are difficult to pay off.

3. Credit cards also differ in the types of services offered; this can be a reason to choose one card over another. Here are some of the services:

- High or no credit limits.
- Rewards for the cardholder such as cash back, gifts, airline miles, or a discount on a new car.
- The number of merchants who accept the card.
- Travel services such as covering the rental car insurance deductible, discounts on hotels, travel-life insurance, or check-cashing privileges.

Question:

a. What characteristics should you look for if you want to save money on a credit card?

NAME: _____ CLASS PERIOD: _____

Reading a Credit Card Statement

A credit card statement reveals a lot about what it costs to charge your purchases and then pay interest on the loan. Let's see what information is found on a typical statement. Take a look at the credit card statement below:

Credit Is U
America's Credit Card Company

Account Number:	000 000 0
Payment Due Date:	2-19-09
Minimum Payment:	23.00
Total Amount Due:	$1,122.85

Cardmember Name:

Tim Gray
333 Palm Way
Oceanview, FL 00000

Amount Enclosed: _____

Mail Payment to: P.O. Box 00000000
                       Newark, DE 19716

Detach and mail this portion with your check or money order ot the address above. Do not staple or fold.

Account Number	Billing Date	Payment Due Date	Days in Billing Period
000 000 0	01-25-09	02-19-09	32

Date	Reference Number	Description	Amount
1-14-09	01010101	CD Haven	22.30
1-21-09	02020202	Pizza, Etc.	8.33

Credit Line: $7,500   **Credit Available: $6,378**

Previous Balance	-	Payments & Credits	+	Finance Charges	+	New Charges	=	New Balance	Min. Payment
$1,072.30	-	.00	+	19.92	+	30.63	=	$1,122.85	23.00

The finance charge is determined by applying a periodic rate of	Which is an ANNUAL PERCENTAGE RATE of	To that part of the balance subject to finance charge of up to	Balance computation methods shown on reverse side
.05754%	21.00%	Entire Balance	Average daily balance

*Purchases, returns, and payments made just prior to billing date may not appear until next month's statement.

Inquiries: Send inquiries (not payment) to: P.O. Box 222, Denver, CO 80202

Notice: See reverse side for important information

Questions:

a. How much did Tim Gray charge on his credit card in the month of the statement?

b. What is the credit limit on this credit card?

c. How much of that credit was available at the time of this statement?

d. How does Tim's previous balance compare to the new balance shown on this statement?

e. Was Tim charged a finance charge this month? If so, what was the amount of the finance charge?

f. What is the annual percentage rate for credit on this account?

g. Looking at this statement, do you think Tim is handling his credit well? Why or why not? What would you recommend?

NAME: _____ CLASS PERIOD: _____

Using a Computer to Calculate Payments for a Loan

Introduction

Computers can be very helpful in figuring out various aspects of a loan. In the following situation, you will be working with mortgages, which are relatively large loans that are used to finance house purchases. Mortgage payments are typically made every month and are extended over many years—often 15 or 30 years.

Mortgages aren't free. Borrowers pay interest on their mortgage loans. And there are costs in addition to interest. Some of these are called closing costs. Closing costs vary from lender to lender depending upon the expenses the lender has for processing mortgage loans.

Let's analyze four different mortgages. These mortgages come with different down payments, different annual interest rates, and different time periods. In each case, however, the homebuyer is purchasing a $175,000 house.

The Four Mortgages

1. Sean and Amber Johnson made a 20 percent down payment and took out a $140,000 mortgage at the local bank. It is a 30-year fixed-rate mortgage with an annual interest rate of 7 percent and closing costs of $4,200.

2. Alvin and Emily Jin qualified for a special mortgage program in which the required down payment is only 5 percent of the cost of the home. They took out a $166,250 mortgage. It is a 30-year fixed-rate mortgage with an annual interest rate of 7 percent and closing costs of $4,987, plus private mortgage insurance (PMI) for 10 years for a cost of $13,133. (When you make a down payment of less than 20 percent, lenders require mortgage insurance. For this insurance you pay an insurance premium each month, along with your mortgage payment, until the equity in your home is equal to 20 percent.)

3. Benny and Silvia Ramirez got a loan through a mortgage broker who found a lower interest rate (6 percent) than the one offered by the local bank. They made a 20 percent down payment and borrowed $140,000 for 30 years. Their closing costs include more fees than they would have paid the bank, but their interest rate is 1 percentage point lower. Their closing costs are $5,000.

4. Emily McGill knows that she can save money by paying off a mortgage quickly. She made a down payment of 20 percent and borrowed $140,000 at a fixed rate of 5.5 percent. Because she will pay off her mortgage in 15 years, her annual interest rate is lower than she would have paid for a 30-year mortgage. The closing costs for this loan are $4,200.

Your Task

Compare these four mortgages by completing the **Mortgage Comparison Table**. Enough information has been provided above for you to fill out most of the table. However, you will need to use a mortgage calculator to determine the monthly payment for each loan. Also, you will need to use the amortization table from the mortgage calculator to determine the total interest that will be paid over the life of each loan.

An additional piece of information has also been provided. Each loan has an APR that represents the true annual interest percentage cost of the loan. Mortgage APRs are calculated by including closing costs and other mortgage-related costs into the effective cost of the loan. You can find mortgage APR calculators online. Determining APR is particularly useful because it enables you to compare interest rates across different types of financing instruments. The Truth in Lending Law requires that the APR be identified for loans.

Using a mortgage calculator is easy. Just plug in the principal, annual interest rate, and term (in years) for each of the four mortgages. Check the monthly payment amounts and use the amortization table to calculate total interest payments. Then use a mortgage calculator and fill in the chart. If your teacher does not provide a website, try www.bankrate.com to calculate the mortgage payment.

Mortgage Comparison Table

	Mortgage 1	Mortgage 2	Mortgage 3	Mortgage 4
Home price	$175,000	$175,000	$175,000	$175,000
Down payment %	20%	5%	20%	20%
Down payment $				
Principal	$140,000	$166,250	$140,000	$140,000
Interest rate				
Term				
Monthly payment				
Total interest				
Closing costs and PMI	$4,200	$4,987 + 13,133 (PMI)	$5,000	$4,200
APR	7.295%	8.058%	6.331%	5.958%
Total payment, down payment, principal, interest, closing costs and PMI				

Questions:

a. If you buy a home and make a relatively small down payment, what happens to the monthly payments and total payment for your loan?

b. What happens to the monthly payment and total payment for a loan with a lower annual interest rate?

c. What happens to the monthly payment and total payment if the term of the mortgage is 15 years rather than 30 years?

d. What is the trade-off if you get a 15-year mortgage rather than a 30-year mortgage?

e. How does calculating APR help you compare the two 30-year loans that have a 7 percent interest rate?

f. How can you reduce your total payment when buying a home?

NAME: _____ CLASS PERIOD: _____

Getting the Best Deal on Your Auto Loan

Jill Winston shopped carefully for a new car.

She found the model she wanted and negotiated a price of $22,000. She applied her old car's trade-in value to the down payment, which came to $5,000. Jill had to borrow $17,000 to buy the car.

Jill knew she should shop for credit just as she had shopped for the car. She took the following steps:

- **Checked her credit rating:** Jill made sure her credit rating was good and that there were no mistakes in her credit report.

- **Made comparisons:** She checked interest rates at her bank and at one other bank. She also checked the rate the car dealer offered. She checked the rates at a finance company that advertised easy terms. Finally, she checked online for car loans offered at several websites.

- **Compared loans for the same time period:** Jill found an array of rates for different time periods. She decided that she should compare the rates for loans for the same time period. She chose a three-year loan because longer loans mean higher total finance charges over the life of the loan. She also thought she might buy a new car in three years, and she wanted the loan to be paid off by then.

What Jill found.

The Last National Bank, where Jill has her checking account, offered her a loan with a 6.65 percent APR and a finance charge of $1,799. An online lending site offered Jill a loan with a 5.27 percent APR and a finance charge of $1,416.17. The car dealer offered her a loan with an APR of 7.24 percent and a finance charge of $1,964.01. Finally, the Friendly Finance Company offered her a loan with an APR of 13.95 percent and a finance charge of $3,901.85.

Comparing the loans.

Fill in the chart below to determine the best loan. Remember that the total cost of the loan is the principal ($17,000) plus the finance charge. For the purpose of this exercise, the monthly payment is the total cost of the loan divided by the number of months (36).

Kind of loan: _____   Principal: _____   Repayment period: _____

Name of Place	APR	Finance Charge	Total Cost	Monthly Payment
Last National Bank				
Online Lending Site				
Car Dealer				
Friendly Finance Company				

Questions:

a. Which loan is the best deal?

b. Which loan is the worst deal?

c. Jill took the best loan. How much extra did she pay because she financed her car instead of buying it for cash?

d. How much money did Jill save by taking the best deal rather than the worst deal?

NAME: _____ CLASS PERIOD: _____

Shopping Online for an Auto Loan

Now it's time to shop online for a loan. Assume you want a loan to buy a new car. You will search for car loans and visit several websites. Your new car costs $20,000. Your trade-in and down payment total $5,000. Therefore, the principal of the loan is $15,000. The payment period is four years. Find four different online offers for a four-year new-car loan and identify the APR for each. You may wish to start by going to www.bankrate.com and checking new-car loans in your area, but check offerings in other areas as well.

Kind of loan: _____ **Principal:** _____ **Repayment period:** _____

Website	APR

Questions:

a. Which loan has the lowest APR?

b. How do the APRs on new-auto loans compare to APRs for used-auto loans?

c. Are the loan rates the same in all areas?

d. Are the loans quoted only in terms of their interest rate, or are there other costs involved?

NAME: _____ CLASS PERIOD: _____

Identifying the True Cost of Car Ownership

Use the Edmunds website calculator, *True Cost to Own,*® at www.Edmunds.com to compare the cost of owning a new car and the cost of owning a two-year-old car of your choice. Please select only one vehicle and compare its cost as a new and a two-year-old car. Use the chart below to record your findings. Answer the questions that follow.

Five-Year Costs of a New Car

	Year 1	Year 2	Year 3	Year 4	Year 5	5-yr Total
Depreciation						
Taxes and Fees						
Fuel						
Maintenance						
Repairs						
Financing						
Insurance						
Tax Credit						
Yearly Totals						

Five-Year Costs of a Used Two-Year-Old Car

	Year 1	Year 2	Year 3	Year 4	Year 5	5-yr Total
Depreciation						
Taxes and Fees						
Fuel						
Maintenance						
Repairs						
Financing						
Insurance						
Tax Credit						
Yearly Totals						

Questions:

a. What are the two biggest expenses in owning a new car during the first five years?

b. What are the two biggest expenses in owning a used car in the first year?

c. What is the total cost of owning the new car for five years?

d. What is the total cost of owning the used car for five years?

e. What is the difference in cost between purchasing a new car as compared to purchasing a two-year-old car?

NAME: _____ CLASS PERIOD: _____

Shopping in Your Community for an Auto Loan

Now it's time to shop for a loan at lending institutions in your community. Some possible places are banks, savings and loans, credit unions, and finance companies. Again assume that you are buying a new car for $20,000. Your trade-in and down payment come to a total of $5,000, and the principal of the loan is $15,000. The repayment period is four years.

Kind of loan: _____ **Principal:** _____ **Repayment period:** _____

Name of Place	APR
1.	
2.	
3.	
4.	

Questions:

a. Which bank offers the lowest APR?

b. Which bank offers the highest APR?

c. Did any lender offer a lower APR if you had a checking or savings account at that institution?

d. Are the loans quoted only in terms of their interest rate, or are there other costs involved?

e. Would you get a better deal from a local lending institution or from an online source?

f. Name one advantage and one disadvantage of shopping for a loan in your local community compared to shopping for a loan on the Internet.

NAME: _____ CLASS PERIOD: _____

Consumer Credit Protection

Credit problems can be an important source of financial difficulty for young adults getting their first taste of financial independence after high school. In 2008, a national survey conducted by Jump$tart Coalition found that most high school students didn't understand the risks involved in using credit cards. Few students knew the maximum they could be forced to pay if they lost their credit card or if it was stolen. Even worse, most didn't understand that the longer they took to pay off their credit card balance, the more they would pay in finance charges.

Young adults today have easy access to credit. Three-fourths of undergraduate college students in 2008 had credit cards. The average balance on these cards was $2,200. Nellie Mae, an organization that makes loans to college students, says that, in addition to credit card debt, many students will have $20,000 in student loans to pay off when they leave college.

As the above information suggests, young adults sometimes make bad choices about spending. They are sometimes inclined to live beyond their means and run up big debts. Excessive credit card debt is a common problem. So are high monthly payments on car loans, high monthly payments for rent, and an inability to save money. For young couples, financial problems are often a troublesome factor contributing to break-ups and divorce.

Financial problems, however, are not reserved for the young. People of all ages can face financial problems. An unexpected illness, the loss of a job, a divorce, or the loss of child care—these and other difficulties can tip a household into financial trouble.

Employers, unions, credit unions and banks may employ staff members who can provide free budget and credit advice. Several non-profit credit-counseling agencies also provide assistance to people who are having difficulty managing their finances. These agencies may be available for face-to-face, telephone, and online counseling.

Not all agencies are the same. If you have occasion to work with a credit-counseling agency, be sure to ask about the counselors' qualifications. Are they accredited or certified by the National Foundation for Consumer Credit (NFCC), Accredited Financial Counselors (AFC), or Certified Financial Planners (CFP)? What services are offered and what are the fees? Make sure the agency will do a full budget review before enrolling you in a debt-management plan. Do you pay anything before you are helped? Are there ongoing monthly fees? Does the agency provide educational materials? Are these materials available on the Internet?

Credit-counseling agencies sometimes work with creditors to create repayment plans that are manageable for their clients. In these cases, all of the client's debt is consolidated into a lump sum, and the client pays one monthly payment on that sum to the counseling agency. The agency ensures that payments will be made to the creditors in a timely manner. Sometimes an agency is able to negotiate reduced interest rates and the elimination of fees. These cost savings allow clients to repay their debt more quickly. Before you enter into a debt-repayment plan ask the following questions: How is your payment determined? How does your debt repayment work? How will you know your creditors are receiving payments? Can the agency get your creditors to reduce interest rates, eliminate interest and finance charges, or waive fees? Are there alternatives to the debt-repayment plan? What happens if you can't keep up with the agreed-upon plan?

Remember: In a credit transaction, both sides expect to benefit. Borrowers expect to use credit to purchase something of value to them today and/or in the future. Lenders expect to be repaid, with interest. If parties to these transactions consistently cheated and lied, the cost of credit would be very high, and few could afford it. The vast majority of credit transactions are ones in which all parties obtain the benefits they sought.

But the world is not a perfect place. Sometimes borrowers make mistakes or are dishonest with lenders. Sometimes lenders make mistakes or are dishonest with borrowers.

Several state and federal laws are designed to protect consumers of credit from dishonest business practices. State credit-protection laws vary, of course, from state to state. You might want to contact your state bureau that handles such matters to learn more. The federal government has several laws regulating consumer credit. These include the Truth in Lending Act, the Fair Credit Reporting Act, the Equal Credit Opportunity Act, the Fair Credit Billing Act, the Fair Debt Collection Practices Act, the Electronic Funds Transfer Act, and the Fair and Accurate Credit Transactions Act.

Federal Consumer Credit Protection

- The **Truth in Lending Act** requires that lenders disclose the cost of credit in simple terms. The lender must state the percentage costs of borrowing in terms of the annual percentage rate (APR), which takes into account all the costs of financing. The lender must also disclose the total finance charges for the loan. The Truth in Lending Act also protects against unauthorized use of credit cards. If your credit card is lost or stolen, you are liable for no more than $50 in charges made by someone else. If you have promptly notified the card issuer of the loss or theft, you cannot be held responsible for any charges after your notification. The Truth in Lending Act also requires that if a business advertises one credit feature (such as how many months to pay, or the amount of the monthly payment), it must mention all other credit terms.

- The **Fair Credit Reporting Act** governs the activities of credit bureaus and creditors. Among other things, the Fair Credit Reporting Act requires creditors to furnish accurate and complete information regarding your credit history. If you are refused credit, you have a right to see your credit report file from the bureau that submitted the negative information on which the refusal was based. The **Fair and Accurate Credit Transactions Act**, an amendment to the Fair Credit Reporting Act, requires that each of the three credit bureaus provide you with a free copy of your credit report each year, upon your request. The three credit reporting agencies, in partnership with the Federal Trade Commission, have established a website that consumers can use to obtain their free credit reports: www.annualcreditreport.com. The Fair Credit Reporting Act requires credit bureaus to investigate if you disagree with information on your credit report. If your claim is valid, your report must be corrected. Finally, the Fair Credit Reporting Act requires that only people with a legitimate business purpose can obtain a copy of your credit report.

• The **Fair and Accurate Credit Transactions Act** also provides protection against identity theft—for example, by placing alerts on credit histories if identity theft is suspected or if a person is deployed overseas in the military. The Act also seeks to reduce identity theft by limiting account information that businesses can print on receipts at time of purchase.

• The **Equal Credit Opportunity Act** requires that all consumers will be given an equal chance to receive credit. The Equal Credit Opportunity Act states that it is illegal to discriminate against applicants for credit on the basis of sex, marital status, race, national origin, religion, age, or because the applicant receives public assistance income.

• The **Fair Credit Billing Act** requires creditors to mail your bill at least 14 days before payment is due. It also establishes procedures for correcting billing errors and fraudulent charges on your credit card accounts.

• The **Electronic Funds Transfer Act** provides protection to people who use ATMs and debit cards. The Act limits your liability if your card is lost or stolen. How quickly you report the loss determines the amount for which you are held responsible. If you report your ATM card lost or stolen within two days of discovering the loss or theft, your losses are limited to $50. (Note that "discovering the loss" can mean when you first notice the card is missing, or it can mean the time when you receive your monthly statement.) If you wait up to 60 days, you are liable for up to $500. If you wait more than 60 days, you could lose all the money taken from your account.

• The **Fair Debt Collection Practices Act** forbids collection agencies from using threats, harassment, or abuse to collect debts. This Act does not apply to creditors who are collecting their own debts.

Questions:

a. What credit problems are common among young adults?

b. What are some common causes of credit problems among people in other age groups?

c. What are some questions you should ask before entering into an agreement with a credit-counseling agency?

d. What levels of government offer consumer credit protection?

e. Why do most credit transactions benefit both the borrower and the lender?

f. Which law protects consumers from unauthorized use of credit cards?

g. Which law forbids collection agencies from using harassment to collect debts?

h. Which law requires creditors to bill you at least 14 days before payment is due?

i. Which law protects users of consumer credit against discrimination on the basis of sex or race?

j. Which law establishes a procedure that consumers may use to correct inaccuracies in their credit reports?

k. Which law allows you to receive one free credit report annually from each of the three credit-reporting agencies?

l. Which law offers consumers some protection when they use a debit card?

NAME: _____ CLASS PERIOD: _____

Credible Credit Counselors

Part 1. Your Job

You are a credit counselor. You specialize in explaining to your clients their rights under federal law, and their responsibilities as borrowers. You offer your customers advice on possible actions they should take in regard to their credit problems. Your teacher will assign two clients to you. After reading each client's case, answer the following questions (you may wish to use Exercise 18.1 to help you answer the questions):

Questions:

a. According to federal law, what are the legal rights of your client?

b. Are your client's legal rights being violated?

c. Is your client being responsible or irresponsible?

d. What should your client do?

Part 2. The Clients

Client 1

I am 18 years old, and I just started college. My parents gave me a debit card. I lost it. I didn't use it much. I didn't know it was lost until my mother called and told me that she found all these outrageous charges on her statement. The card was used to charge stuff costing more than $5,000. Mom said she contacted the card issuer the day she found out about the outrageous charges—which was about three weeks after I must have lost the card.

Client 2

I am 23 years old and a recent graduate from a technical school. I have my first office job. I have fallen behind in making payments on my car loan. My bank has contacted a collection agency to collect the money I owe. Now, I don't answer the telephone. The collection agency calls me every hour of the day and night. I am getting some of these calls at work, and it is embarrassing to have other people see the messages left by the collection agency. Keeping this job is my best chance to pay off the car loan. Even with the job, however, it will take a few more weeks for me to start making payments again.

Client 3

I am 21 and I have a new apartment. Now I am looking for a new sofa. I was reading newspaper ads to see what financial terms I could get if I bought a new sofa. One full-page ad caught my attention. It said, "No money down, pay only $9.99 a month." I thought this sounded too good to be true, but the ad said nothing more about how much the sofa costs, how many monthly payments I would have to make, or the interest rate I would have to pay. If I buy this sofa, I am afraid I might have to face some hidden costs.

Client 4

I am 31 years old and I recently separated from my spouse. I applied for a credit card in my own name. Today I received a letter from the credit card company. It said, "We are sorry. Your application for credit has been denied." How could that be? I have always paid my bills on time. My former spouse sometimes had credit trouble, but I did not. The letter was no help at all.

Client 5

I am 22 years old. I reached into my pocket today and my wallet was gone. I don't know exactly when it disappeared. I could have lost it when I was in a crowded movie theater a couple of nights ago. I lost $75 in cash, my driver's license, and two credit cards. I am going to the Department of Motor Vehicles today to get a new driver's license. I will get around to calling the credit card people in a few days.

Client 6

We are a newly married couple. We are shopping for a car and a loan with which to buy the car. The first lender we spoke to told us that the interest rate for the loan was only 7 percent. However, in addition to the interest charged on the loan, there would be a loan fee of $200. Can lenders charge fees like that?

Client 7

I am 35 years old. I received a call last week from a cell phone company about an overdue bill on an account that wasn't mine. Someone stole my information and used it to get a cell phone. The company said sometimes hackers are able to get into your computer when you are using an unsecured WI-FI connection in an airport or restaurant. I wrote the phone company and told them that the account was not mine and that I would not pay the charges. They agreed to dismiss the charges. I also contacted the credit bureaus and told them I was a victim of identity theft. I asked them to send me a copy of my credit report and to put a fraud alert on my account so that no new accounts could be opened until I was contacted.

NAME: _____ CLASS PERIOD: _____

Legal Protection for Borrowers

Directions: Listed below are several problems. Place a check mark in the correct column to indicate which federal law addresses the problem.

Federal Legislation ➡ Problem ⬇	Truth in Lending Act	Fair Credit Reporting Act	Equal Credit Opportunity Act	Fair Credit Billing Act	Electronic Funds Transfer Act	Fair Debt Collection Practices Act	Fair and Accurate Transactions Act
1. A collection agency is making harassing telephone calls about a debt.							
2. A creditor refuses to give you credit because you receive public assistance income.							
3. Your credit card is lost or stolen; you are liable for $50 of charges made by someone else.							
4. A creditor refuses to lend to you because you are African-American.							
5. A bank refuses to tell you why you were turned down for credit.							
6. You disagree with statements made in your credit report.							
7. You are liable for $50 on your debit card if a loss or theft is reported immediately.							
8. The first bill for your car payment arrives and you realize that you have only five days to pay it.							
9. A creditor tells you that the interest rate for vacation loans is only 7% per month.							
10. You see charges on your credit card that are not yours.							

NAME: _____ CLASS PERIOD: _____

Scams and Schemes

Millions of credit transactions are completed each day. In the vast majority of cases, both parties to these transactions benefit. But the world is not a perfect place. The credit industry, like any other industry, has a few people who operate on the edge. Some of these people are flat-out thieves. Others operate businesses that, while completely legal, can put people who are already in financial trouble into positions from which they will find it even more difficult to recover.

Not all financial scams and schemes involve credit. Some deal with investments. They appeal to your desire to make a bundle of cash overnight. But, if any sales pitch sounds too good to be true, it probably is.

Here are some of the more common scams and schemes.

1. What Is Identity Theft?

Can you be electronically kidnapped? Yes. Scam artists get your name, Social Security number, credit card number, or some other piece of personal information. They use this information to open a new credit card account using your name, date of birth, and Social Security number. When they use the credit card and don't pay the bills, the failure to pay is reported on your credit report. The scammers also may call your credit card issuer and, pretending to be you, change the mailing address on your credit card account. Then they will make charges on your account. Because your bills are being sent to a new address, you may not realize there's a problem. Scam artists can do all sorts of other damage. They might open cellular phone service in your name. They might open a checking account in your name and write bad checks. Identity theft is illegal.

How do these thieves get your information? They might steal your wallet or mail or even your trash! If you have thrown out (and not torn up) credit card offers, bills, bank statements, and receipts, thieves may recover what you have dumped and use the information from your trash to open new accounts. **Skimming** occurs when your debit or credit card numbers are stolen while you are using your card. **Phishing** is the scam whereby thieves pretending to represent banks or other companies send you printed materials or pop-up messages that ask you for account information. **Pretexting** occurs when thieves request your information from financial institutions, phone companies or other sources, under false pretenses. Hackers set up free WI-FI sites in public places so that they can gain access to your computer while you are on unsecured connections.

How do you find out that you are a victim of identity theft? Often it is after some damage has already occurred. You may receive bills for accounts you never opened. You may apply for a loan and be denied. When you view your credit report, you may see overdue debts that aren't yours.

How can you repair the damage done by ID theft? Four steps must be taken after your identity is stolen.

- Review your credit reports and place a fraud alert on your credit report so that you will be contacted before any new accounts are opened in your name. Any of the credit-reporting agencies can help place the fraud account with all three agencies.
- Close the accounts that have been altered or opened fraudulently.
- File a complaint with the Federal Trade Commission. They will work with other agencies and law enforcement officers to try to find the thieves.
- File a report with your local police or the community where the theft took place. You may need a copy of this report to help you dispute things like fraudulent charges to your old accounts or new accounts opened with your information.

For more information on identity theft, go to the Federal Trade Commission's website, www.ftc.gov.

2. What Is a Loan Scam?

An advertiser runs an ad offering a personal-debt consolidation loan, taking all your credit payments and rolling them into one. Rarely is a company name or street address given. Instead, the "lender" has an 800 or 900 telephone number for consumers to call. When you call, the company representative asks only for minimal information about the loan you want and about your financial history. He or she explains that you will be called back to indicate whether or not the loan has been approved. As part of the scam, all the loans are approved. The consumer is then instructed to send in a fee in return for the promised loan. The loan, of course, never arrives. A loan scam is illegal.

3. What Is a Credit-Repair Scheme?

A company advertises that it can erase your bad credit history or remove bankruptcy from your credit records. The company requests that a fee be paid up-front for which the company promises to "repair" the consumer's credit report. However, there is little, if anything, such a business can do to "repair" a customer's poor credit record. There are no quick or easy ways to repair a poor credit history. A credit repair scheme is illegal.

4. What Is a College Financial-Aid Scam?

A company advertises that millions of dollars in scholarships go unclaimed every year. The company promises that it will do the research needed to find you a scholarship. The company requests that a fee be paid up-front, usually $200-$400. The company promises that if it can't find a $2,000 scholarship, it will return the fee. What will you get in return if you pay the fee? Probably some scholarship information that is available from public sources at no cost to anyone who wishes to look. Guidance counselors and college financial-aid officers are good sources of reliable scholarship information, available at no charge to you. The college financial-aid scam is illegal.

5. What Is a Pyramid Scheme?

A pyramid scheme comes disguised as a system for selling goods. Participants are recruited by advertisements offering big profits to people who pay a fee for agency rights—that is, rights to sell goods as representatives of the pyramid company. Each recruited agent then recruits others to join, with each new participant also paying a fee. The key to the scheme is that early participants receive commissions on any sales they make, plus payment for recruiting additional members. The problem is that there will not be enough new members to keep the pyramids growing steadily for even a few months. When the flow of new members dries up, the pyramid collapses. Pyramid schemes can take several forms. They can be disguised as games, buying clubs, chain letters, mail-order operations, or multi-level business opportunities. A pyramid scheme is illegal.

6. What Is a Payday Loan?

A payday loan allows a person to get cash for use until his or her next payday, with no credit background check. It is a legal loan, and it can help some people in an emergency. An applicant for a payday loan typically provides paycheck stubs, savings account numbers, and checking account numbers to the lender. Upon receiving the loan, the applicant also writes a postdated check and gives it to the lender. This check is written for more money than the amount of the loan. It is postdated so that it can be cashed later—generally two weeks after the loan is made. The lender cashes the check after the date on the check. In this way, the lender is repaid for the loan issued, with interest. Typically, the interest rate (APR) is quite high. The APR may be 300 percent or higher. Why would anybody borrow money at an interest rate of 300 percent? Probably because the borrower in question has an urgent need for money. Also, the borrower probably believes that the high interest rate won't matter much because the loan will be paid off quickly. But it is easy for people in financial trouble to fall behind in paying off a payday loan. They sometimes wind up taking out another payday loan, and then another. Soon the finance and interest payments add up to more than the amount of money they borrowed. Payday establishments are found across the country. They are legal.

7. What Is a Rent-to-Own Company?

Rent-to-own companies rent and sell appliances, furniture, and electronic products to consumers. Typically, a consumer agrees to rent something for a short period—one week or a month. If the consumer rents the product for a specified period of time (often 18 months), she or he will become the owner of the product—either automatically or by making an additional payment. Rent-to-own is a legal business. It affords consumers some advantages, such as returning an appliance or furniture item after a short period of time. How might this business practice become a scheme? Purchasing merchandise from a rent-to-own company usually costs two to five times as much as purchasing the same goods from a department store or appliance store. If the difference in the total payments and a fair price for the product were expressed as an interest rate, the rate would commonly be over 100 percent.

Match the Scam/Scheme

Directions: Match the name of the scam/scheme in the column on the left to one of the definitions below.

Scam or Scheme	Definition
Rent-to-own	
Credit-repair scheme	
College financial-aid scam	
Pyramid scheme	
Payday loan	
Identify theft	
Loan scam	

A. A fraudulent company offers to erase a consumer's bad credit history or remove bankruptcy information from the consumer's credit records. It collects an up-front fee, and it can in fact do nothing to "repair" a consumer's poor credit record.

B. A fraudulent company offers to find a student a scholarship. It collects an up-front fee and fails to provide the scholarship.

C. Scam artists get your name, Social Security number, credit card number, or some other piece of your personal information and use this information to open a new credit card account, cellular phone account, or checking account.

D. A fraudulent company offers a personal debt consolidation loan, collects an up-front fee, and never provides the loan.

E. A legal loan that allows a person to get cash until payday, with no credit back-ground check. Typically, the interest rate (APR) is quite high.

F. A fraudulent company in which the first participants receive payment for recruiting additional members.

G. A legal scheme offered by some businesses whereby the consumer pays a very high price for appliances, furniture, and electronics products because the consumer first rents an item and then buys it.

NAME: _____ CLASS PERIOD: _____

Name That Scam

Directions: Read each scam or scheme described in Column A and match it to one of the names of the scams listed below. Place the letter of the correct answer in Column B.

A. Identity theft

B. Loan scam

C. Credit-repair scheme

D. College financial-aid scam

E. Pyramid scheme

F. Payday loan

G. Rent-to-own plan

Column A	Column B
1. Make big money on your home computer. Join our eel burger distribution network. Cash in on this new health food craze. E-mail your friends. They can be distributors too.	
2. Need cash today? Can't wait until you get paid? You can get $50 to $500 in 15 minutes. No credit checks!	
3. Tired of the broken-down MP3 player with lousy speakers? Want to step up to a new system but are short of cash? We can make it happen today!	
4. Here is the deal of a lifetime guaranteed to make you and your friends rich in weeks. Pay $100 to play Jack Pot. In weeks you will make hundreds more. Don't miss out. This is your chance!	
5. You receive an outrageous telephone call from the collection agency saying you have failed to pay a bill for nearly $20,000. You explain that the correct name was used but the billing address for the account was wrong. Soon you hear from a bank in another state that you are overdrawn by $5,000 in a checking account you didn't know you had.	
6. Credit problems? You need not suffer forever! Let us help. We can remove bankruptcies, liens, and bad loans from your credit file forever! Join our hundreds of satisfied customers.	
7. Over your head in debt? Bill collectors harassing you? Can't sleep? We can help. We can find credit for you. It's guaranteed! Call 1-800-123-4567.	
8. Every year, thousands of college scholarships go unclaimed. Are you skimping along simply because you don't have "connections"? We can help. We guarantee you that we will find you a $1,000, $2,000, or even a $5,000 scholarship. All your money is returned if you are not satisfied!	

Introduction

Saving and Investing

Have your parents ever told you that money doesn't grow on trees? This is good advice as far as it goes. Money most definitely doesn't grow on trees, but it can grow. It grows when you save and invest wisely. If you want to be wealthy, start by saving and investing regularly. Begin saving now and save as much as you can afford. Pay yourself first by putting money into a savings account, money market fund, or some other investment instrument every time you are paid. Because of the power of **compounding,** your money will grow big time.

Compounding means that you earn interest on the interest earned in previous years. For example, if you save $2,000 and earn 8 percent in annual interest, you will have $2,160 at the end of the first year. You will have earned $160 in interest. The second year, however, you will earn more than $160 in interest because you will earn 8 percent of $2,160, not $2,000. This will come to $172.80 in interest, or $12.80 more than the first year.

So you earned $12.80 more the second year. Big deal. How much difference does this compounding make? If you save $2,000 a year at 8 percent annual interest from age 22 to age 65, you will have saved $86,000 over 43 years. How much money would you have at age 65? You would have a total of $713,899, or $627,899 more than you saved. Think of compound interest as the fertilizer that makes money grow. (Example from Dwight Lee and Richard McKenzie, *Getting Rich in America.*)

Of course, with a higher rate of return, money grows even faster. An 8 percent annual rate of return may not be as difficult to achieve as you might think. The value of stocks has increased more than that, on average, over the last 60 years.

But the people competing for your savings will not pay you a high interest rate out of kindness. Saving and investing will not only enrich you; your investment dollars also help businesses and the economy grow. That's why banks, savings and loan associations, credit unions, governments, and companies pay you for the use of your money. They hope to gain by using your savings.

Some of these people competing for your savings will be taking more risks than others. They pay more to get you to take more risk. Risk is the chance that you might not get your money back. The higher the risk, the higher the potential reward. You might want to take some high risks with some of the savings, but not with all of it. That is why you need to **diversify** your investments. Diversification means that you should not put all your eggs in one basket–that is, not all your savings in one investment instrument. Although diversification will not guarantee that your investment will not lose money, it should decrease the chance of that happening.

Money can work for you, but you will have to work to make it grow as much as possible, consistent with the risks you are willing to take. Investigate before you invest. There are millions of places to invest, from very safe insured savings accounts to speculative stocks, commodity futures, and collectibles. A successful investor learns a lot before making investment choices. The lessons that follow will get you started, but you will never be able to stop learning if you want to invest successfully over your lifetime. There is a pot of gold at the end of the rainbow, but getting there takes hard work.

THEME 5 | Lesson 20: What's the Cost of Spending and Saving?

EXERCISE
20.1

NAME: _____ CLASS PERIOD: _____

The Benefits and Opportunity Costs of Spending and Saving

A person's income represents some of his or her financial resources. Because of limited financial resources, every decision about the use of resource involves an oppurtunity cost. The opportunity cost is what you give up when you make a choice. It is the most-valued option that you refused because you chose something else. It is your next-best option.

One important choice that everyone faces is whether to consume goods and services today or to consume goods and services later. Spending today brings immediate benefits or gratification. The opportunity cost of spending today is that your spending will leave you with less money to buy goods and services in the future. Saving builds wealth, enabling you to buy goods and services in the future—perhaps a car, a college education, a house, a vacation. The opportunity cost of saving is that saving leaves you with less money to use for buying goods and services today.

Questions:

a. What are the benefits and the opportunity cost of spending your income today?

b. What are the benefits and opportunity cost of saving some of your income?

EXERCISE 20.2

THEME 5 | Lesson 20: What's the Cost of Spending and Saving?

NAME: _____ CLASS PERIOD: _____

A Tale of Two Savers

The following case study is about two people who saved money. Both of them earned 10 percent interest on the money they saved. (Of course, in the real world, the interest or rate of return on savings can differ greatly from year to year and from one savings institution to another.)

Ana Gutierrez started saving when she was 22 years old, right out of college. Saving involves an opportunity cost—the next-best alternative given up. It wasn't easy for Ana to save $2,000 a year then, considering her car loan, the expenses of operating her car, and rent payments. But Ana was determined to save because her grandmother always said it isn't what you make, but what you save, that determines your wealth. So, reluctantly, Ana gave up buying that new car and renting a really nice apartment, and she saved $2,000 a year. After 12 years, she got tired of the sacrifice, yearning for a brand new red sports car and other luxuries. She didn't touch the money she had already saved because she wanted to be sure she would have money for retirement, which she planned to do at the end of her 65th year. But she quit saving and hit the stores.

Shawn Wright didn't start saving until he was 34 years old. He also graduated from college at 22, but he had done without many things in college, and, once he found a job that gave him a decent income, he wanted to have some of those things he had done without. He bought a new car, a very nice wardrobe, and he took some wonderful trips. But spending his income involved an opportunity cost. By the time he was 34, Shawn was married; he had many responsibilities, and he decided he'd better start saving and planning for his financial future. He also had heard that it isn't what you have earned, but what you have saved, that determines your wealth. He figured he had 25 to 30 productive years left in his career. So, with new determination, Shawn saved $2,000 a year for the next 32 years until he retired at the end of his 65th year.

Which person do you believe had more savings at the end of his or her 65th year? Ana or Shawn?

Now let's see what really happened. Using information from the table at the end of this exercise, answer the following questions.

THEME 5 | Lesson 20: What's the Cost of Spending and Saving?

EXERCISE
20.2

Questions:

a. How much money had Ana put into savings by age 65?

b. How much money had Shawn put into savings by age 65?

c. How much in total savings (wealth) did Ana have at the end of her 65th year?

d. How much in total savings (wealth) did Shawn have at the end of his 65th year?

e. In money terms, what was the opportunity cost of Ana's savings decision? What was the benefit?

f. In money terms, what was the opportunity cost of Shawn's savings decision? What was the benefit?

g. In trying to build wealth, the amount saved is obviously important. What other factors are important? Why?

h. What are the incentives for saving early in life?

i. What was Ana's opportunity cost of saving early?

j. What conclusions can you draw from this activity?

EXERCISE 20.2

THEME 5 | Lesson 20: What's the Cost of Spending and Saving?

The Growth of Ana's and Shawn's Savings

Age	Interest rate	Ana Gutierrez			Shawn Wright		
		Saved	Interest Earned	Total saved at the end of the year	Saved	Interest Earned	Total saved at the end of the year
21	10%	$0.00	$0.00	$0.00	$0.00	$0.00	$0.00
22	10%	$2,000.00	$200.00	$2,200.00	$0.00	$0.00	$0.00
23	10%	$2,000.00	$420.00	$4,620.00	$0.00	$0.00	$0.00
24	10%	$2,000.00	$662.00	$7,282.00	$0.00	$0.00	$0.00
25	10%	$2,000.00	$928.20	$10,210.20	$0.00	$0.00	$0.00
26	10%	$2,000.00	$1,221.02	$13,431.22	$0.00	$0.00	$0.00
27	10%	$2,000.00	$1,543.12	$16,974.34	$0.00	$0.00	$0.00
28	10%	$2,000.00	$1,897.43	$20,871.78	$0.00	$0.00	$0.00
29	10%	$2,000.00	$2,287.18	$25,158.95	$0.00	$0.00	$0.00
30	10%	$2,000.00	$2,715.90	$29,874.85	$0.00	$0.00	$0.00
31	10%	$2,000.00	$3,187.48	$35,062.33	$0.00	$0.00	$0.00
32	10%	$2,000.00	$3,706.23	$40,768.57	$0.00	$0.00	$0.00
33	10%	$2,000.00	$4,276.86	$47,045.42	$0.00	$0.00	$0.00
34	10%	$0.00	$4,704.54	$51,749.97	$2,000.00	$200.00	$2,200.00
35	10%	$0.00	$5,175.00	$56,924.96	$2,000.00	$420.00	$4,620.00
36	10%	$0.00	$5,692.50	$62,617.46	$2,000.00	$662.00	$7,282.00
37	10%	$0.00	$6,261.75	$68,879.21	$2,000.00	$928.20	$10,210.20
38	10%	$0.00	$6,887.92	$75,767.18	$2,000.00	$1,221.02	$13,431.22
39	10%	$0.00	$7,576.71	$83,343.84	$2,000.00	$1,543.12	$16,974.34
40	10%	$0.00	$8,334.38	$91,678.22	$2,000.00	$1,897.43	$20,871.78
41	10%	$0.00	$9,167.82	$100,846.05	$2,000.00	$2,287.18	$25,158.95
42	10%	$0.00	$10,084.60	$110,930.65	$2,000.00	$2,715.90	$29,874.85
43	10%	$0.00	$11,093.06	$122,023.71	$2,000.00	$3,187.48	$35,062.33
44	10%	$0.00	$12,202.37	$134,226.09	$2,000.00	$3,706.23	$40,768.57
45	10%	$0.00	$13,422.61	$147,648.69	$2,000.00	$4,276.86	$47,045.42
46	10%	$0.00	$14,764.87	$162,413.56	$2,000.00	$4,904.54	$53,949.97
47	10%	$0.00	$16,241.36	$178,654.92	$2,000.00	$5,595.00	$61,544.96
48	10%	$0.00	$17,865.49	$196,520.41	$2,000.00	$6,254.50	$69,899.46
49	10%	$0.00	$19,652.04	$216,172.45	$2,000.00	$7,189.95	$79,089.41
50	10%	$0.00	$21,617.25	$237,789.70	$2,000.00	$8,108.94	$89,198.35
51	10%	$0.00	$23,778.97	$261,568.67	$2,000.00	$9,119.83	$100,318.18
52	10%	$0.00	$26,156.87	$287,725.54	$2,000.00	$10,231.82	$112,550.00
53	10%	$0.00	$28,772.55	$316,498.09	$2,000.00	$11,455.00	$126,005.00
54	10%	$0.00	$31,649.81	$348,147.90	$2,000.00	$12,800.50	$140,805.50
55	10%	$0.00	$34,814.79	$382,962.69	$2,000.00	$14,280.55	$157,086.05
56	10%	$0.00	$38,296.27	$421,258.96	$2,000.00	$15,908.60	$174,994.65
57	10%	$0.00	$42,125.90	$463,384.85	$2,000.00	$17,699.47	$194,694.12
58	10%	$0.00	$46,338.49	$509,723.34	$2,000.00	$19,669.41	$216,363.53
59	10%	$0.00	$50,972.33	$560,695.67	$2,000.00	$21,836.35	$240,199.88
60	10%	$0.00	$56,069.57	$616,765.24	$2,000.00	$24,219.99	$266,419.87
61	10%	$0.00	$61,676.52	$678,441.76	$2,000.00	$26,841.99	$295,261.86
62	10%	$0.00	$67,844.18	$746,285.94	$2,000.00	$29,726.19	$326,988.05
63	10%	$0.00	$74,628.59	$820,914.53	$2,000.00	$32,898.80	$361,886.85
64	10%	$0.00	$82,091.45	$903,005.99	$2,000.00	$36,388.68	$400,275.53
65	10%	$0.00	$90,300.60	$993,306.59	$2,000.00	$40,227.55	$442,503.09

THEME 5 | Lesson 20: What's the Cost of Spending and Saving?

EXERCISE
20.3

NAME: _____ CLASS PERIOD: _____

Why It Pays to Save Early and Often

Suppose you put $1,000 into an investment that earns 10 percent interest. You leave the $1,000 there for 10 years. You might expect to have earnings of $1,000 or a total of $2,000 in your account ($1,000 x .1 x 10 = $1,000). Adding the $1,000 in earnings to your original $1,000, you would end up with $2,000, right?

Wrong! You would have more than that. The return would be much higher because you would earn interest not only on the original $1,000 but also on the interest earned along the way over the 10 years. This sort of interest is called **compound interest**. Here's how compounding works. Let's assume that 10 percent interest is compounded annually. This first year you earn $100 in interest. Now you have $1,100. The second year you earn interest on $1,100 ($1,100 x .1 = $110), and that amount is added on to your principal.

As interest compounds, savings grow. How long would it take for the savings of our hypothetical saver to double if he didn't spend any of those savings? You can find out, approximately, by dividing 72 by the interest rate (expressed in percentage form). This procedure is called using the **Rule of 72**. For example, at 10 percent interest, money will double in about 7.2 years if the interest is compounded (72 ÷ 10 = 7.2 years).

Let's see how long it will take money to double in other cases. Do the calculations and fill in the answers in the right-hand column below.

Investments	Interest or rate of return	Years to double
Passbook savings	3%	
Money market account	4%	
U.S. Treasury bond	6%	
Stock market	9%	

Because of compounding, it pays to save early and often. Early opportunity costs can bring large benefits. These are the factors that affect the growth of savings:

• The earlier or longer you save, the more savings you will have.

• The more income you save each year, the more savings you will have.

• The higher the interest rate or rate of return, the more savings you will have.

Question:

a. One key point in the economic way of thinking is that people respond to incentives. What is the incentive for saving early and often?

NAME: _____ CLASS PERIOD: _____

Types of Investment Risk

People save and invest their money to receive a return on their savings or investment. In this exercise, we will call any type of saving or investing an "investment." The return is the income earned from the investment; it is usually calculated on a yearly or annual basis. That return can be stated as a percentage of the amount invested. Then it is called the annual rate of return.

Risk comes from the uncertainty about whether you will receive the promised return. The greater the risk you take with your investment, the higher the potential rate of return. Unfortunately, with more risk, it is also more likely that you will lose money. In other words, you can expect a return from taking risks with your money, but you could also take a financial loss. As with any economic decision, there is no free lunch in deciding about investments. Here are some of the risks you take when you invest your money.

Financial Risk

Financial risk is the risk that the business or government that you have invested in will not be able to return your money—much less pay a rate of return. Businesses, state agencies, and local governments have declared bankruptcy on some past occasions. The U.S. government is unlikely to become bankrupt, so investing in U.S. government savings bonds carries very little financial risk. Insured accounts in banks, savings and loan associations, and credit unions are insured by the Federal Deposit Insurance Corporation (FDIC) up to $250,000, so they carry no financial risk.

Market Risk

Market risk is the risk that the price of an investment will go down. This doesn't usually happen to money saved at a bank, savings and loan association, or credit union. However, the prices of stocks, bonds, and mutual funds are determined by supply and demand, and they do go down (as well as up). The **supply** of an investment refers to the different quantities of that investment that will be offered for sale at various prices during a specific time period. The **demand** for an investment refers to the different quantities of an investment that investors are willing and able to purchase at various prices during a specific time period. The equilibrium price is the price at which buyers want to buy the same amount of an investment that sellers want to sell. The important point is that anything that changes the behavior of buyers and sellers can change the price of an investment. For example, technology stocks have been "hot" at various times. Prices increased because more people wanted technology stocks at various price levels (demand increased). When investors became less interested in technology stocks, the average price fell because fewer people wanted technology stocks at every price level (demand decreased). Investors' expectations of the future earnings of companies play a large role in the value of stocks. When company earnings fall below what investors have expected, it is common for the stock price to fall. In recent years, there have been occasions in which "bubbles" seem to have appeared in the stock market. These bubbles represent stocks whose value is overly inflated relative to companies' fundamental value. It is difficult to know for sure when a bubble appears, but when a bubble does appear there is significant market risk that the bubble will burst, causing a decline in stock prices.

Liquidity Risk

Liquidity is the ability to turn your money into cash or spendable funds. Checking accounts, for example, offer high liquidity. Some investments are very liquid. Savings accounts generally allow you to withdraw your money at any time without a penalty. Stocks listed on a stock exchange are very liquid; you can buy or sell them at any time (although you may have to take a less favorable price). Real estate and collectibles, on the other hand, are not very liquid because it takes time for a seller to find a buyer. Although the Internet is speeding up this process, there is no guarantee that a buyer and seller can get together on price and other terms for the sale of real estate and collectibles.

Inflation Risk

People invest money today in order to have that money, and more, available to spend in the future. The goal is to receive the original investment back plus a return, so that you will be able to buy more in the future. Inflation can decrease the value of your investment. When you save or invest, you are deferring your spending until a later time. If prices rise over that time, your money will not go as far as it would have gone earlier. Therefore, investors are more interested in the real rate of return than the nominal rate of return. The **real rate of return** is the **nominal rate of return minus the inflation rate.** For example, let's say you put your money in a certificate of deposit at a 5 percent rate of return. The annual rate of inflation is 3 percent. Therefore, your real rate of return is 2 percent (5 percent – 3 percent = 2 percent). In general, the longer the time period, the greater the likelihood that purchasing power will decrease because of inflation, and the greater the inflation risk.

Fraud Risk

Some investments are misrepresented. In these cases, information about the investment is designed to deceive investors. Anyone can print a fancy brochure, make promises on the telephone, or guarantee great returns on the Internet. Criminals often make up facts that turn out to not be true. Therefore, it is important to investigate before you invest. Most investment fraud occurs in securities and savings schemes that do not involve banks, savings and loan associations, credit unions, and brokerage firms.

Questions:

a. What is the annual rate of return on an investment?

b. If you earn $40 a year on a $500 investment, what is the annual rate of return?

c. What is the relationship between the expected rate of return and the investment risk?

d. If the annual nominal rate of return on an investment is 10 percent and the annual rate of inflation is 3 percent, what is the real rate of return?

e. True, false, or uncertain, and why? "The Internet is the future of our economy. The prices of Internet stocks are bound to go up."

f. True, false, or uncertain, and why? "This investment pays 30 percent a year and is perfectly safe. I put my mother's money into this investment."

NAME: _____ CLASS PERIOD: _____

The Pyramid of Risk and Rewards

Highest Risk: Highest Potential Return or Loss

Speculative
Stocks

Real Estate

Individual Stocks

Stock Mutual Funds

Money Market Mutual Funds

Insured Certificates of Deposit

Insured Savings Accounts

U.S. Savings Bonds

Lowest Risk: Lowest Potential Return or Loss

The figure above ranks investments according to their risks and rewards. The higher an investment is on the pyramid, the greater the risk. Because the risk is greater, the potential rewards and potential losses are also greater.

Your job is to rank each of the investments on the following pages on a 1-3 scale, with 1 representing the lowest risk or reward and 3 representing the greatest risk or reward. Circle the number that best represents each risk or reward. For each choice, explain your answer.

Mattress

You could hide your money under a mattress.

Financial Risk	1	2	3	**Why?**
Market Risk	1	2	3	
Liquidity Risk	1	2	3	
Inflation Risk	1	2	3	
Reward	1	2	3	

Regular (Passbook) Savings Account

The Federal Deposit Insurance Corporation (FDIC) insures savings accounts for up to $250,000. Interest rates on these accounts are usually lower than rates for other savings and investment choices, but you can open an account with very little money and you can withdraw your money whenever you like.

Financial Risk	1	2	3	**Why?**
Market Risk	1	2	3	
Liquidity Risk	1	2	3	
Inflation Risk	1	2	3	
Reward	1	2	3	

Certificate of Deposit (CD)

CDs are a special type of savings deposit that you must leave in the bank for a set amount of time, during which you receive a fixed rate of interest. The FDIC also insures these accounts for up to $250,000. Banks usually require that you deposit at least $500 in a CD. If you withdraw your money before the end of the agreed-upon time, you must pay a penalty—usually in the form of forgone interest earnings.

Financial Risk	1	2	3	**Why?**
Market Risk	1	2	3	
Liquidity Risk	1	2	3	
Inflation Risk	1	2	3	
Reward	1	2	3	

Money Market Mutual Funds

These funds are sold by investment companies that pool investors' funds and use the funds to purchase very safe and very liquid short-term financial products offered by businesses and governments. For every dollar put in such a fund, an investor can expect to get back a dollar plus interest. Although money market mutual funds are not insured by the federal government, they are low-risk investments. Interest rates are usually higher than rates on bank accounts but lower than returns for stocks and bonds bought and held for the long term. Investors can get their money out of a money market mutual fund at any time. Some funds also allow investors to write checks on their accounts.

Financial Risk	1	2	3	**Why?**
Market Risk	1	2	3	
Liquidity Risk	1	2	3	
Inflation Risk	1	2	3	
Reward	1	2	3	

Stocks

Stocks are shares of ownership in a corporation. When you buy stock, you take the risk that the value of the company might decline. Such a decline would reduce the value of your ownership stake. Some stocks make quarterly payments to investors, which are called dividends. Your return for stock ownership will vary, depending on what happens to the prices of the shares and the dividends received. Stocks on exchanges such as the New York Stock Exchange and NASDAQ can be bought and sold whenever the exchange is open. The amount of money you need to buy stock depends on the prices of the stocks you want to buy and the number of shares you want.

Financial Risk	1	2	3	**Why?**
Market Risk	1	2	3	
Liquidity Risk	1	2	3	
Inflation Risk	1	2	3	
Reward	1	2	3	

U.S. Government Savings Bonds

You can buy savings bonds from the federal government for as little as $25. You can't sell these bonds to other people, but the government will redeem them after they have been held for a minimum amount of time. If you need to sell them before maturity, there may be a penalty in the form of loss of interest.

Financial Risk	1	2	3	**Why?**
Market Risk	1	2	3	
Liquidity Risk	1	2	3	
Inflation Risk	1	2	3	
Reward	1	2	3	

Stock Mutual Funds

Stock mutual funds are offered by investment companies that pool funds from individual investors to purchase stocks. The risk depends on the investment objective. Some funds invest in high quality, blue-chip stocks; others invest in more speculative stocks. The major difference in buying a fund rather than individual stocks is that you indirectly own many stocks in a mutual fund, and you don't have all your eggs in one basket. Therefore, the risk is lower than the risk that comes with owning an individual stock. You can sell your shares in the fund back to the fund company at any time.

Financial Risk	1	2	3	**Why?**
Market Risk	1	2	3	
Liquidity Risk	1	2	3	
Inflation Risk	1	2	3	
Reward	1	2	3	

Stock Index Funds

Stock index funds are mutual funds that invest in groups of stocks that mirror segments of the stock market. For example, an S&P 500 index fund would invest in the companies in the S&P 500 index—primarily large-cap U.S. stocks. Index funds require no selection or decisions by fund managers, so they have lower fees than other mutual funds. Index funds outperform managed funds most of the time. Index funds provide diversity and high performance with relatively low fees. They are a great choice for individual investors.

Financial Risk	1	2	3	**Why?**
Market Risk	1	2	3	
Liquidity Risk	1	2	3	
Inflation Risk	1	2	3	
Reward	1	2	3	

Real Estate

Most investors in real estate buy the house they live in. Houses can increase in value, but housing prices can also fall. Sometimes when prices do rise, they rise less than the inflation rate. To sell your house, you must find a buyer. Many buyers and sellers use real estate brokers.

Financial Risk	1	2	3	**Why?**
Market Risk	1	2	3	
Liquidity Risk	1	2	3	
Inflation Risk	1	2	3	
Reward	1	2	3	

NAME: _____ CLASS PERIOD: _____

An Introduction to Stocks and Bonds

There are many different ways to invest your money. Each of them has different levels of risk and potential return. Stocks and bonds are two common types of financial investment.

A bond can be thought of as similar to a loan or an IOU. When you purchase a bond, you are lending money to the corporation or government entity that issued the bond. In return you receive interest payments on the bond. These payments are based on the original value (called the face value) of the bond and the interest rate (called the coupon rate) that existed when the bond was issued. Because bonds can be traded in secondary markets after they are issued, the price of bonds (and the yield they earn) can differ from the face value (and the coupon rate).

Shares of stock represent ownership in a corporation; they are often referred to as equities. Returns on investments in stocks result from changes in the stock price and/or from dividends. Some companies pay dividends (which are quarterly payments to stockholders) and others do not. Stocks can appreciate, or go up in value, as profits are earned and future expectations for growth of the company are positive. Stocks can also depreciate, or go down in value, if the company suffers losses or, in the extreme, goes bankrupt.

The graph on the following page charts the average annual performance of four different stock and bond investments over the 20-year period from 1989 to 2009. These four different investments represent the performance of four separate funds that are managed by Vanguard, a well known financial services firm that offers a variety of mutual funds. In the graph, the Vanguard 500 Index fund invests in the stock of 500 of the largest U.S. companies. The Vanguard Total Bond Market Index fund is comprised of a mix of U.S. government and corporate bonds. The Vanguard International Value fund represents investments in a set of foreign companies, and the Vanguard Asset Allocation fund attempts to balance stocks, bonds, and other investments to maximize long-term returns.

The annual return on stocks has historically averaged around 10 percent. The bar graph clearly shows that you won't earn that rate of return every year. Some years it will be higher and other years it will be lower. However, if you invest for the long term, you may be able to achieve performance that is close to this historical average.

NAME: _____ CLASS PERIOD: _____

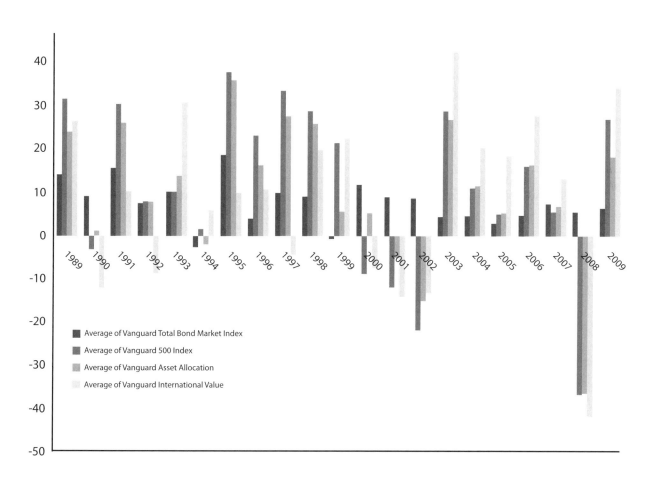

Average of Vanguard Total Bond Market Index
Average of Vanguard 500 Index
Average of Vanguard Asset Allocation
Average of Vanguard International Value

Questions:

a. During the 20 years examined in the graph above, is there one type of investment that consistently outperformed the other types of investment?

b. Which fund appears to have the steadiest rate of return over the 20-year period?

c. What are the highest and lowest rates of return for the bond market fund?

d. Since 2003, which fund appears to have had the most volatile annual return?

e. The historic average annual rate of return in the stock market from 1927 to 2009 was nearly 10 percent. The historic average annual rate of return on bonds over this same period was approximately 5 percent. Since 1989, in how many years did the Vanguard 500 Index fund outperform the Vanguard Total Bond Market Index fund?

f. In how many years did the Vanguard 500 Index fund have a negative return?

g. In how many years did the Vanguard Total Bond Market Index fund experience a negative return?

h. If you had to select between investing in the Vanguard Total Bond Market Index fund and the Vanguard 500 Index fund, which fund would you choose? Why?

NAME: _____ CLASS PERIOD: _____

What Investment Strategy Is Best for Me?

What Investment Strategy Is Best for Me?

If you were to ask Warren Buffet, one of the most successful investors of all time, "What investment strategy is best for me?" he would reply in the way he has replied many times: "The best way, in my view, is to just buy a low-cost index fund and keep buying it regularly over time." In this lesson, we will discuss the three key elements of Mr. Buffet's advice: "index funds," "low-cost," and "buying regularly over time."

What Is an Index Fund?

First let's review what a mutual fund is. A mutual fund is a collection of stocks, bonds, or other investments selected and managed by a fund manager to meet certain investment goals. Investors buy shares in these funds, often for a relatively low price; in doing so, they diversify their investments, since their purchase gets them pieces of all the fund's holdings. Investors in managed funds pay for the services of the fund manager. These fees typically range from 1-3 percent. So, for each $100 you invest, you pay the fund manager $1-$3. This may not seem like much, but these fees can add up to thousands of dollars over time.

Index funds are mutual funds that make up a market index. They provide diversification by purchasing all of the stocks or bonds in a market index. An example would be investing in all the stocks in the S&P 500 Index (the most commonly traded large-cap stocks in the United States). Index funds don't need a manager to select or manage investments—they are defined by whatever is in the index. The fees, accordingly, are relatively low, typically ranging from 0.15 - 0.5 percent. That's as little as 15 cents per $100 invested!

You might think that paying a fund manager to buy and sell stocks in a mutual fund would give you an advantage–that the manager's special knowledge and diligence would pay off and enable you to beat the performance of the indexes or the market average. But most managed funds do not perform as well as their target benchmark over time. In buying into a managed fund, an investor may well pay more and get less.

How Can I Keep Costs Low When Investing?

Invest in no-load funds with low management fees that don't have 12b-1 fees.

• **Loads:** Mutual funds that charge a fee to purchase shares are called load funds. Load funds charge a sales fee or commission that occurs "up-front."

- **Redemption fee (Back-end load):** a sales charge or fee that may be charged when you sell your shares. This is known as a back-end load. These charges typically decline with each year you own shares in the fund, and they disappear after you own shares for a specified number of years. If you buy and sell shares through a stockbroker (or others who are authorized to buy and sell securities), there may be an additional sales charge from that professional.

- **12b-1 fee:** The Securities and Exchange Commission (SEC) allows mutual funds to charge what is known as the 12b-1 fee to cover marketing and distribution costs. This fee helps pay the costs of buying and selling securities within the fund's portfolio (in lieu of sales charges or loads), advertising, and other costs.

- **Management and other fees:** All mutual funds charge investors a management or administrative fee that compensates the portfolio manager(s). This management fee is typically stated as a percentage, but it may also be stated as a flat fee. Other fees cover the cost of maintaining an office, fees paid to companies contracted by the mutual fund to provide services for shareholders, and other fund operating expenses.

- **No-load:** There are a number of mutual funds that don't charge fees to buy or sell shares. These funds are called no-load funds. There is no evidence that load funds outperform no-load funds.

To reduce their costs, many investors avoid load funds and those that charge 12b-1 fees. And they look for funds with low management fees (0.5 percent or less). The idea is to use money to buy shares, not to pay fees.

How Can I Buy Regularly Over Time?

Use dollar-cost averaging.

Dollar-cost averaging is an investment strategy in which you invest a set dollar amount on a regular basis no matter what the market is doing. The idea is that no one can predict the market. Many investors feel it is best to keep buying on a regular basis in order to achieve returns that are similar to long-term stock returns. The easiest way to make regular investments is through a payroll deduction.

For example, you invest $50 per month in a mutual fund regardless of the share price. The result is that you purchase more mutual fund shares when the price is low and fewer shares when the price is high.

EXERCISE 22.2

What's Anne's Dollar-cost Average?

Anne purchases $100 worth of mutual fund shares on a quarterly basis for one year. The share prices have gone up and down over the 12-month period. The results of her purchases are found in the table below. Note that by dollar-cost averaging, she is paying an average cost of $4.53 per share and she is able to take advantage of periods when the share price is low to accumulate more shares.

Amount Invested	Price per Share	# of Shares Purchased
$100	$2	50.0
$100	$5	20.0
$100	$10	10.0
$100	$12	8.3
$400		88.3

Average Cost per Share = Total Amount Invested ÷ Total Number of Shares Purchased = $400/88.3 shares = $4.53 per share

Kelly invests $50 every month. The prices of her mutual fund shares have changed during the year. The table below shows her monthly purchases.

Amount Invested	Price per Share	# of Shares Purchased
$50	$10	5.00
$50	$8	6.25
$50	$6	8.33
$50	$4	12.5

Questions:

a. How many shares did Kelly purchase over four months?

b. What was her average cost per share over this period?

NAME: _____ CLASS PERIOD: _____

How Much Will My Investment Be Worth?

Potential returns for different investments vary significantly. Since 1926, the average return on U.S. Treasury bills and other cash equivalents like savings accounts has been 3.7 percent. The average annual return on long-term government bonds during the same period has been 5.4 percent. Large company stocks, like those in the S&P 500 index, have averaged an annual return of 10.2 percent. It is important to understand what average return means—i.e., that in some years these investments made money and in some years they lost money. Remember the investment pyramid from **Exercise 21.2**: higher returns are associated with higher risk.

Use the following website http://partners.leadfusion.com/tools/motleyfool/savings02/tool.fcs to estimate how much money you would earn if you invested $100 per month for 20 years in each of the investments listed in the table below. Assume you are paying no taxes and that the rate of inflation is 3 percent. Enter the value of your investment in the table below and answer the question at the end of the exercise.

How Much Will My Investments Be Worth?

	U.S. Treasury Bills	Long-term Government Bonds	Large Company Stocks
Amount Invested	$100	$100	$100
Average Annual Rate of Return	3.7%	5.4%	10.2%
Additional Deposit	$100	$100	$100
Frequency	Monthly	Monthly	Monthly
Years Invested	20	20	20
Federal or State Tax	0	0	0
Inflation Rate	3%	3%	3%
Value of Investment After 20 Years			

Question:

a. What is the benefit of putting some of your money into riskier investments, such as stocks, for long-term goals such as retirement?

NAME: _____ CLASS PERIOD: _____

The Rule of 72

The Rule of 72 is a guideline for determining approximately how many years it will take an investment to double in value. It can also be used to determine the interest rate that would be needed for an investment to double in value after a given period of time.

To calculate the number of years required for an investment to double in value, you divide 72 by the annual interest rate (expressed in percentage form).

For example: Freddy invests $1,000 at 3 percent interest in a money market account. He wants his money to double to $2,000. It will take approximately 24 years for his money to double in value. 72/3 = 24 years.

To find the interest rate you need to earn for an investment to double, divide 72 by the number of years you have until you need the money.

Another example: Patrick has $1,000 to invest. He would like it to double in 10 years. He needs an interest rate of 7.2 percent to double his money in 10 years. 72/10 = 7.2 percent.

Now you try it!

a. George has $700 in an account earning 10 percent. How long will it take to double his money?

b. Jay wants his money to double in eight years. What interest rate does he need to earn?

c. Gennie wants to buy a home in five years. She needs a $10,000 down payment. At what interest rate will her $5,000 double in five years?

NAME: _____ CLASS PERIOD: _____

Investment Bingo

There are 24 terms below the bingo board. From the list below, write one term in each square so that you have 24 different terms on your board.

		Free Lunch		

Dollar-cost averaging	Compound interest	Wealth/Net worth
Incentive	Income	Market risk
Rule of 72	Financial risk	Fraud risk
Liquidity risk	Real rate of return	U.S. Savings Bond
Nominal rate of return	Passbook savings account	Inflation risk
Certificate of deposit	Inflation	Stocks
Money market mutual fund	Stock mutual fund	Annual rate of return
Real estate	Opportunity cost	Risk/Reward ratio

NAME: _____ CLASS PERIOD: _____

How Much Risk Am I Willing to Take?

OK, so now you know about some important investment possibilities. How do you know where to put your money? For short-term goals—goals you'd like to reach within a year or two—it's best to put your money into savings instruments like certificates of deposit (CDs) or a savings account. With those savings instruments, there is no risk that you will lose any of your principal. You will earn some interest, and it's not likely that inflation will take too large a bite over such a short period of time.

For long-term goals, such as saving for your child's college or for retirement, you have time to take more risk. Just how much depends on your personal risk tolerance. Take the Investment Risk Tolerance Quiz at http://njaes.rutgers.edu/money/riskquiz to find out your preference for risk when investing, as well as your preferences for investment alternatives.

Risk tolerance score _____

What are some investments that meet your preference for risk?

NAME: _____ CLASS PERIOD: _____

How Do I Allocate My Investments?

Diversification requires investment in different segments of the economy. Typically, however, the percent of an investor's portfolio allocated to each of the different segments varies over time. Financial advisors help clients determine how to allocate their investments based on their long-term and short-term goals. When you are young, you can afford to have a higher percentage of your portfolio invested in mutual funds based on stocks or stock indexes. As you approach retirement, your portfolio should become more conservative, with a higher percentage of your portfolio in bonds and other lower-risk financial instruments. Use the Asset Allocator website at http://www.ipers.org/calcs/AssetAllocator.html to estimate what a portfolio would look like for the following clients:

Client 1

Mario, age 25, is a recent college graduate with a job in media relations. While he currently doesn't have any assets, he plans to begin investing $2,000 this year through his 401(k). He expects to continue this practice throughout his working lifetime. He has many choices for investing his money, and he is interested in what you think a good mix might be for a young person just starting out. Mario's marginal tax rate is 15 percent. He does not need money from investments to supplement his income at this time. He has a high tolerance for risk and he expects that the economic outlook will be average during the years in which he will invest.

Draw a pie chart to indicate what Mario's asset allocation should be. Indicate the percentage invested in each instrument.

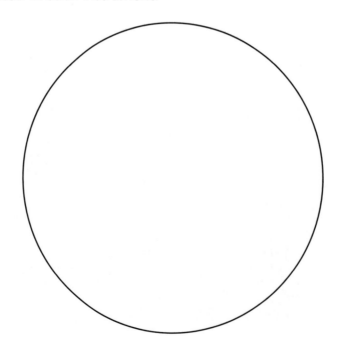

Client 2

Sofia is a 45-year-old teacher. She started saving later in life and now has $54,000 to invest. She saves $2,500 each year. Her marginal tax rate is 25 percent. She is saving for retirement and does not need to draw any income from her investments at this time. She gets a sick feeling in her stomach at the thought of losing her hard-earned money. Her risk tolerance is medium-low. She will continue to work for several years before retirement; she expects the economic outlook to be average during most of the years in which she will be investing.

Draw a pie chart to indicate what Sofia's asset allocation should be. Indicate the percentage invested in each instrument.

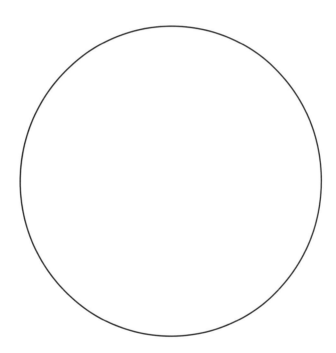

Client 3

Ray is 65 years old. He plans to retire at age 67. He's saved for most of his life and now has $625,000 that he would like to invest with you. He is unsure what the best investments would be for him at this time of his life. He saves $2,000 each year; he is in the 28 percent marginal tax bracket. Since he is getting ready to retire, he will soon need income from his investments to support him in retirement. He is a risk taker, but he thinks that at this time in his life he should invest conservatively. He would describe his risk tolerance right now as low. He is an optimist and expects the economic outlook to be good in the next few years.

Draw a pie chart to indicate what Ray's asset allocation should be. Indicate the percentage invested in each instrument.

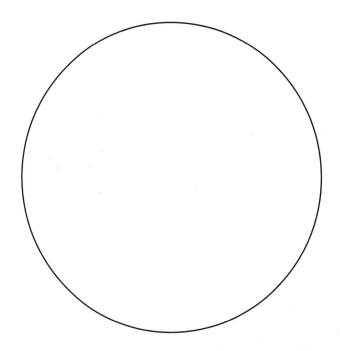